MASS VIOLENCE IN AMERICA

MASS VIOLENCE IN AMERICA

THE BURNING OF THE CONVENT

Louise Goddard Whitney

ARNO PRESS & THE NEW YORK TIMES

New York • 1969

Editorial Note

Nations, like men, are sometimes interested in burying the past.

In early 1968, after more than five years marked by political assassinations, racial uprisings, campus disorders, mass demonstrations and the violent suppression of protest, *The New York Times Magazine* asked a group of distinguished scholars to reply to the question, "Is America by nature a violent society?" In answer, University of Chicago anthropologist Clifford Geertz wrote:

> "We do not know very well what kind of society we live in, what kind of history we have had, what kind of people we are. We are just now beginning to find out, the hard way . . ."

The proposition was astonishing but correct: what was least understood about domestic political violence was its role in American history. It was common knowledge that the United States had had a Revolution, a Civil War, some trouble with the Indians and a period of labor-management conflict. But one could search the shelves of the nation's great libraries without discovering more than a handful of works on the subject of violence in American history, and these hopelessly out of date.

Historians had generally ignored or soft-pedaled the history of farmer uprisings, native vigilantism, labor-management struggles, ethnic conflicts and race riots; comparative work in the history of social conflict was particularly weak. Sociologists and political scientists in the grip of "consensus" theory tended to treat episodes of mass violence in America as insignificant or aberrational—temporary exceptions to the norm of peaceful progress. Psychologists and behavioral scientists discussed "mob violence" in terms which suggested that riots, revolts, insurrections and official violence were the products of individual or group pathology. All such interpretations had the effect not only of minimizing group violence in America, but of depriving it of political content—hence, of relevance to the present.

As a result, as late as 1968, the rich, multifarious and often terrifying history of domestic political violence was still largely *terra incognita*. So long as most Americans wished to keep certain skeletons locked away in their closets, few scholars would attempt to open doors. Conversely, once the American people, frightened yet emboldened by the sudden reappearance of intense social conflict, began to ask new questions about the past, so did the scholars.

Our purpose in helping Arno Press and *The New York Times* select and publish significant documents in the history of political violence has not been to compound past errors by overemphasizing the role of conflict in American history. On the contrary, our aim has been to provide materials which will aid in the search for an accurate perspective on the present. MASS VIOLENCE IN AMERICA includes eyewitness reports, government documents and other descriptive and analytic material relating to mass political violence in the United States. These documents not only provide information—they give the "feel" or "flavor" of past eras of civil disorder by evoking the emotional and political context in which revolts took place. Most of them have long been out of print and are obtainable, if at all, only in the nation's largest libraries.

The scope of this series is wide, ranging from accounts of Indian warfare to descriptions of labor-management violence, from narratives of colonial insurrections to reports on modern racial uprisings. It is not, however, limitless, nor were the constituent volumes carelessly selected. The principle of coherence which guided the selections is implicit in the phrase "mass political violence." "Mass" denotes activity engaged in by large groups rather than individuals acting alone; "political" suggests a relationship between such activity and competition among domestic groups for power, property and prestige; and "violence" is narrowly construed as resulting in physical damage to persons or property. In short, the materials reproduced herein are intended to illuminate the resort to violence by American groups seeking to change or to preserve the status quo. Although historical, they are of interest to any who wishes to understand the causes, nature and direction of domestic political violence, whether they be social scientists, historians or just interested Americans.

Of course, we are particularly hopeful that these volumes will prove useful to those now engaged in curriculum-revision and the teaching of high school and college courses in the area of American studies. What Christopher Jencks and David Reisman term "the Academic Revolution" has made difficult demands on all educators, not the least of which is the demand for courses which are both relevant to the condition of modern America and of the highest academic quality. These volumes are meant to provide raw material for such courses— primary source matter which will help both instructors and students to deepen and enrich their views of the American experience.

Most important, the editors and publisher recognize that these volumes appear during a national crisis which is also a crisis of the spirit, a time in which the public response to various manifestations of civil disorder is increasingly governed by anger, fear and hysteria. In such an atmosphere it is important to recognize that one is not alone in time—that such events have taken place before in America and, unless fundamental changes in our social and political life take place, will probably recur in the future. Our fondest hope is that this work, and others like it, will help to keep alive, in a time of growing unreason, the spirit of reasoned inquiry.

RICHARD E. RUBENSTEIN
The Adlai Stevenson Institute
Chicago, Illinois

ROBERT M. FOGELSON
Harvard-MIT Joint Center
for Urban Studies
Cambridge, Massachusetts

THE BURNING OF THE CONVENT

THE

BURNING OF THE CONVENT.

———

A NARRATIVE OF THE DESTRUCTION, BY A MOB,
OF THE URSULINE SCHOOL ON MOUNT
BENEDICT, CHARLESTOWN, AS
REMEMBERED BY ONE
OF THE PUPILS.

———

CAMBRIDGE, MASS.:
PRINTED BY WELCH, BIGELOW, AND COMPANY.
1877.

INTRODUCTORY.

WHILE the present generation was still in its infancy, Mount Benedict took its place among the storied hills of Charlestown, Mass., — *the three B's,* — a hill of battle, like Bunker and Breed, only the battle had its origin in religious instead of political differences, and bigotry made the attack and won the victory. I was one of the vanquished on this occasion, being at that time a small child.

So many years have elapsed since the event, — which, besides, was followed by no results appreciable by the multitude, — that I dare say few persons at present know that the finest Ursuline Convent in New England was once established on Mount Benedict, in Charlestown. It was built expressly for a boarding-school, and intended for the children of rich men, Protestants preferred. It was, for those days, — I am speaking of the early part of this century, — an immense structure, perfectly furnished and appointed for the purpose; and a body of Irish Nuns, educated in French convents, were imported to give the instruc-

1

tion. Nearly the whole of Mount Benedict was enclosed for the use of the Convent; there was a lodge, a Bishop's house, several terraced walks, and grounds tastefully laid out, for the recreation of the pupils. No such elegant and imposing building had ever been erected in New England for the education of girls. Picturesque on the summit of the hill, with a background of trees, and a foreground of green terraces bordered with shrubbery which descended to the road, its many-windowed façade, glowing in the light of the setting sun, was a sightly object to the good citizens of Boston, returning from their afternoon drive into the suburbs.

"The Convent" soon became a very popular school with these "solid men of Boston," and elsewhere, — even from the extreme north and south of the country. Girls were sent from Canada for the benefit of a warmer climate, and from New Orleans that they might be braced by a cooler atmosphere. The conventual school-system had great attractions for parents brought up under stern Puritan restrictions, against which their daughters were beginning to rebel; but it was an odd idea to call in Catholic discipline as a substitute for Puritan restraints which they could enforce no longer. My father, who believed in the widest liberty for men, was always lamenting the growing independence of women, and the difficulty he found in keeping his daughters under the old rule of implicit obedience; and as soon as I was old enough to be sent from home, he resolved to put me into the Ursuline school on Mount Benedict, Charlestown, there to remain till I was twenty years of age, — happy in the belief that the Nuns could save him the trouble of educating me in habits of strict submission to authority.

Nearly fifty years have elapsed since the day when my mother told me that I was to be sent to "the Convent" boarding-school. I remember it, because to hear the news I was ordered in from the garden, where I was comfortably keeping house under a tall currant-bush, with a gooseberry-bush wash-house attached, on whose thorns my doll's wardrobe was drying. They twitched my sandy locks, and wounded my still more sandy fingers, as I literally tore myself away to obey the summons.

Nearly fifty years! and it happened that on the anniversary of that very day, I, an *almost* old woman, broken down in health, found myself driving with my husband in Charlestown, and passing along the very base of Mount Benedict. That hill still wore its respectable crown of ruins, an unusual ornament in our country, and the ascending terraces were still well-defined, though the plan of the old pleasure-grounds was obliterated by time. For everything had heretofore been allowed to remain just as the hands of the mob left it, the Catholics having indulged themselves in the expensive luxury of retaining the Convent property as a memorial of Protestant bigotry. But, to my astonishment, on this day of which I speak, I saw that the base of Mount Benedict was swarming with sudden life; a steam-paddy had already made a breach in it, and was hard at work, storming it vigorously, assisted by an army of Irishmen with dump-carts. The hill had evidently been secularized, sold, and was in process of grading; religious resentment could not always stand before the rise in real estate.

When I saw the work of levelling the hill fairly under way, I began to wonder how long it would be before the story of the destruction of the Convent by a mob would be forgotten in the neighborhood when those reminder ruins were removed and their site covered with blocks of houses. Probably Catholics would not be allowed to forget it, for *they* were the martyrs; but Protestants would be glad to lose the memory of that singular outburst of bigotry. Then we " fell on talk " regarding the events of that August night of riot, and my husband was surprised to find how accurate was my remembrance of my own small part in the drama, and he made me promise to write down my recollections thereof. So, without further preface, here is the

STORY OF THE DESTRUCTION OF THE URSULINE
CONVENT ON MOUNT BENEDICT, ON THE NIGHT OF
AUGUST 11, 1834, AS REMEMBERED BY A VERY SMALL
EYEWITNESS.

IT was in June, 1834, that my mother told me I
was to enter the Convent as a pupil as soon as
the summer vacation should be over. Dr. Lyman
Beecher was the individual who fixed the time of my
entrance; during the previous winter he had been denouncing fiercely " the Devil and the Pope of Rome "
in a course of lectures in Boston upon Romanism,
exciting a strong feeling against Catholics and all their
ways. My father was a Unitarian, violently opposed
to Orthodoxy, and a spirit of antagonism to Dr.
Beecher led him to carry out at that time the plan he
had long formed for my education in a convent.

In a few days after this had been announced to
me, I remember that a Convent school-circular appeared in the house, which my mother and I studied
zealously. It was ornamented by a vignette of the

building, in which the three principal doors, at the
head of three lofty flights of stone steps, were very
prominent. Four ladies, sitting quite at their ease
in a barouche, spite of the galloping of their horses,
appeared driving up to the middle door, while the
Charlestown stage (omnibuses were not in those
days), in a cloud of dust, and crowded with pupils,
was seen modestly drawing up to a side-entrance.
I. was never weary of gazing upon this wonderful
work of art, nor of reading the circular over and
over, till I knew it by heart.

The school, according to that document, was divided into two sections, Senior and Junior, — terms
which inspired me with great respect, nor could I
imagine myself putting on the dignity proper even
to a Junior. Classes and studies were elaborately
set forth, the names of sundry of the text-books
being past my powers of pronouncing, even with
the help of the dictionary. The pupils were allowed
only to spend one Sunday in a month out of the Convent, either with their parents or guardians, and my
prophetic imagination warned me that each month
would seem a compressed eternity. Sunday duties
were defined in deference to Protestant prejudices ;
the pupils were expected to attend Morning Mass,
but Protestants might read their own Bibles during
the ceremony. Owing, perhaps, to the Puritan strict-
ness of home, — for, notwithstanding my father's Uni-

tarian belief, he thought it conducive to discipline to keep the Sabbath as it was kept in his youth, — I did not value that privilege, as my mother assured me I ought to do, nor yet the prospect of committing chapters to memory on Sunday afternoons, which indulgence the circular also promised to Protestant children. In my heart I suspected that the Catholic pupils had the easiest Sundays to bear.

It was a relief to turn from those gloomy paragraphs in the circular to those which treated of *dress;* this matter was discussed with a seriousness befitting the greater importance of the subject. The pupils were expected to dress in uniform: blue merino frocks, darker blue wadded pelisses, beaver bonnets trimmed with blue, was the wear for winter; and pink calico, as the best washable color, for summer, with white frocks for "best," black silk capes and aprons, and straw bonnets trimmed with pink. No wonder I remember the details, for my mother read them over and over in every tone of voice, from defiance to despair and from despair to submission, in view of the trouble and expense involved in preparing such an outfit for me. Mrs. Richards the dressmaker, who worked for the family one month in spring, another in fall, made her appearance, with topless thimble and dangling pinball, to sew for me *alone.* Pink gingham garden-aprons and "cape-bonnets" were also insisted upon

by the circular, and as many under-garments indi-
cated as were then thought necessary for a bride.
And such a fabulous number of stockings was required, that my soul was disquieted within me by
visions of future darning; I had been used to sharing
a limited supply of hosiery with a sister about my
size, and we had divided the task of mending them
between us.

During these days of preparation we were compelled, sorely against the grain, to perform daily
long "stints" of hemming, for an outfit of sheets,
pillow-cases, towels, napkins, etc., was required of
each pupil; but we were allowed to take our sewing
and our little chairs to the platform of the garden-
pump, and tell stories to each other, under the shade
of a crab-apple tree, whose fruit was in a promising
state of sourness.

It was a sad reflection that I should be away at
school when those crab-apples became ripe, but my
sister promised to keep my share for me in the bottom of a battered coal-hod in the garret. Last of
all, a bottle of Kidder's indelible ink was exhausted
in a grand *marking*, and piles of white work occupied every sunny window in the house.

I am afraid to say how much money was spent
in school-books for my benefit, as my father actually
got every series used by the different classes of pupils
through the whole course of study, as given in the

circular, — I suppose to convince himself that he was really disposing of me for years to come.

My mother used to sit up at night and sew cloth covers on the books, and write my name therein in her handsome "hand o' writ." "Sufficient for the day was the evil thereof," I thought, and I declined to look into them till I should be compelled to do so in progress of time. Then came the arduous task of packing my trunk, which my mother accomplished on her knees, and with as much care as if I had been going to Pekin instead of to Charlestown, only four miles off. The sole piece of finery admitted — a pink sash to wear with the white frocks — lay on the top, and I endeavored to draw from it all the consolation it was capable of affording, as my mother forbade me to take playthings or story-books to school. I had wasted enough time over them, she thought, and I was now to be introduced to the stern realities of life.

My father drove me over in the chaise to Charlestown, to introduce me to my future home and teachers a few days before the term began. Wretched, depressing necessity! I remember, as we slowly ascended Mount Benedict by the driveway, comparing the real appearance of the Convent with my recollection of the vignette which ornamented the circular. The building did not seem quite so high, or the doors so broad, or the flights of steps — veritable

Jacob's-ladders in the vignette — quite so lofty. I
missed the barouche and the stage, but, to make
amends, the Lady Superior's coach was at the main
door, with two fat horses and a fat coachman, all as
motionless as those in the vignette. My father instantly drew up to the carriage, and jumped out of
the chaise. I felt by instinct that this was *an occasion*. The door opened, and the Superior appeared,
coming down the steps. She was of medium height
and very stout, but she had the quick step and
vivacious air of a French-Irish woman, and she carried herself with a royal uprightness and dignity
that compelled deference from all who approached
her. Servants followed her with shawls, cushions,
and parcels, and their deferential manner made her
grand air more apparent. I observed that the coachman lowered his head on his breast as the Superior
drew near, that my father bowed lower and lower,
that she addressed him as a queen would address a
subject, that a word was said about me, that the
lady's eagle eye was turned upon me for a moment,
whereupon *my* head also fell upon *my* breast. A
slight bustle, — I remember the Superior got into
her coach while my father was hesitating as to
whether it would be proper for him to assist her,
— a slamming of carriage doors, and with a solemn
jog-trot the fat horses bore away their mistress.
Nobody was permitted to use the grand entrance

but the Superior and the Bishop; my father and I
were ushered into the Convent by a portress at a
side door, and shown to the "parlor." As usual
in convents, a grating separated the guests' division
of the apartment from that appropriated to the *Ré-*
ligieuses who came in to attend visitors. The solemn portress, who looked as if the muscles of her
face were stiffened for want of smiling, bade us sit
down, in a sepulchral whisper, and vanished as if
shod with felt. A great bell clanged through the
carpetless house, and I set myself to watching the
darkness, that to my eyes, fresh from the light of a
summer noon, seemed to be condensed behind the
opposing iron bars. A faint rustle quickened my
attention, a black figure moved through the darkness in wavering lines, stopped at the middle of the
grating, and a beautiful face looked out of it. The
"garb" of the Superior had not impressed me much,
it made but a faint blot on the outdoor sunshine,
but the black setting to Sister Mary Benedict's face
and figure, as seen behind the grating, had a sombre
effect. Young as I was, the Sister's beauty struck
me at once, and I pitied her for having to muffle it
up in such a gloomy head-gear. My father did not
appear to find it disfiguring, however; his manner
was expressing great admiration, I thought, and I
wondered how the Sister could keep her eyes cast
down so steadily, and the muscles of her face so

motionless, and how she managed to speak without parting her lips.

Again there was a word said by my father about poor little me, and I was summoned to stand close to the grating, so that Sister Mary Benedict's downcast eyes might rest upon me easily. A white hand stole out from the black hanging sleeve, and placed itself on my head. I raised my eyes anxiously to her face, not expecting in my humility to meet a glance of approbation, but longing for one little look of sympathy, homesick as I was already by anticipation. Alas! I might as well have sought for it in *a* face of stone, and I felt instinctively that her soul as well as her body was shut out from me by an immovable barrier.

I returned home from this introductory visit to my future abode with a heart as heavy as lead; my dear sister flew to meet me, and to ask me a thousand questions about my experiences, and I could only weep bitterly as I assured her that I *knew*, I was *certain*, I was going to be wretched at the Convent. I could not answer her anxious "Why, but why?" I *felt* my reasons, but I could not put them into words; I had a conviction that, like "Chicken Little," I was going to a place where I had "no business to be," and I felt new anguish in parting with all that my soul held dear. I had a grand wash of my doll's clothes, which were put away in a candle-box. I even washed and ironed the ribbons which my yellow kitten wore round her neck, and I nearly killed my black rabbit by stuffing him too often with fresh clover in my farewell visits. I so longed for something to happen which would prevent my going to the Convent that I almost expected a miracle would be wrought in my favor, nor did I neglect natural means. I am ashamed to say that I ate green apples and sat in draughts, vainly hoping that I might fall ill, and be kept at home to take castor-oil and rhubarb.

There really seemed to be opposition in the air to my going. Several gentlemen called on my father during the few last days of my stay at home, for the purpose of talking to him about the Convent, as I fancied from sundry overheard sentences. It seemed very natural to my childish mind that the public should interest itself in a matter that concerned me so deeply. I lingered near my father when these talks were going on; as well as I could make out by paying strict attention, I learned that *something* had occurred which made the Superior gracious to my father when he met her entering her carriage on the day of our visit, and unusually gracious also to others, and which caused her to show herself more than usual by driving about the country and stopping at the houses of her friends. That same *something* caused Sister Mary Benedict, the most beautiful and fascinating of all the Nuns, to be sent constantly to see visitors in the parlor, and that *something* inspired her to be more charming to them than ever. Then allusions were made to a young girl who had written a lying book, but my father would never let me listen long enough to arrive at the heart of the mystery. He held consultations in a low voice with my mother; I hoped they would end in a reprieve from school, yet I had a sickening feeling that my new books and clothes had cost too much to be given up unless the equivalent money could be miraculously restored to my father's pocket.

After all, nothing occurred to prevent my going, and I was taken to the Convent, punctually, on the appointed day. The last things put into my trunk were the inevitable silver spoons, fork, and mug, usually the only valuable furnishings of a boarding-school table. I was too heavy-hearted at the moment of leaving home to weep; I had put my doll to sleep for a month's nap; I was already looking forward to my return at the end of that time, and my sister promised she should not be disturbed. That faithful friend also declared she would nurse my kitten even in preference to her own, and that my black rabbit should be fed first. How differently I should have felt, as I gave my sister the last solemn kiss of parting, could I have foreseen that before my doll's first monthly nap was over I should have left the Convent forever, and that the place itself would be wiped out of existence. I may as well relate here the events that were working out the ruin of the Convent, — events resulting in sorrow and misery, even death, to some of the victims, but bringing happiness to *one* little girl.

Among the foreign customs retained in the Ursuline school, which fascinated plain Protestants by its novelty, was the pleasant one of holding annually a high state-festival day, called "Coronation day," just before the commencement of the summer vacation. On that day only, parents and guardians passed the limit of the parlor, and were allowed admission to the school-rooms. The music and dancing-rooms were prettily decorated, and furnished with rows of seats, which were crowded with delighted elders, who forgot the heat of a July day in admiring the proficiency of the pupils in the accomplishments taught in the Convent. There were performances on the harp and guitar, as well as on the piano, by curled darlings, dressed in the prescribed white frocks and pink sashes. Drawings, landscapes in India-ink, and fancy-work were handed about, and high art was represented by theorem-paintings, Grecian ditto, and painting on velvet. There were part-songs, recitations, and little dramas performed ; the results of the yearly examinations were made public ; and, last of all, there was a grand mustering of the white frocks and pink sashes on the platform, from the midst of whom a queen was chosen, not by her schoolmates, but by the Nuns, who led her forward to the front of the platform, and

presented her to the public as the prize scholar of the
year, averaging first both in lessons and deportment.
As it was never known beforehand on whom the
choice would fall, this was a moment of great excitement to the pupils, and to the queen herself perhaps
the proudest moment of her life. Then there was a
Coronation, — a crown of beautiful white artificial
flowers, made by the Nuns, was put upon the queen's
curls, she was led to her throne, which was, after a
while, transferred to the head of the long table in
the Refectory, on which a magnificent collation was
spread. The meagre diet of a year was forgotten in
the splendor of this repast, wherein figured every indi-
gestible delicacy that French confectioners could devise
to tempt the palates of the children. Some of the
Nuns were accomplished confectioners, — Paris-trained,
as the school legends ran, — and it was a wonder that
they did not forget an art practised only once a year.

Sister Mary John, the Mother-Assistant, as she was
called, standing next in rank to the Superior and her
natural successor, was the principal teacher of music
at the Ursuline Convent. On her had devolved the
musical training of the pupils for the last fête-day
which was ever held at the Convent, and which happened a few weeks before the time of my entrance as
a pupil. She had been overworked throughout the
year, having had an unusual number of scholars, and
the final labors of " Coronation day " were too much

for her weary frame. A frightful headache seized her
even before the children dispersed on the evening of
that day for the summer vacation, which terminated
in brain-fever and delirium. Though tenderly nursed
and closely watched, she contrived, one hot day, when
doors and windows were left open, to elude the vigi-
lance of her nurses, and to make her escape into the
world, poor thing! in her nightgown. She flew,
ghost-like, down the long slope of Mount Benedict,
and rushed into the first house outside the Convent
precincts, a farm-house occupied for many years by
Mr. Cutler, and situated on the main road. Though
a Yankee and a Protestant, he was a good neighbor
to the Ursuline community, for he let them alone se-
verely; but when this fever-stricken apparition with
wild eyes and shorn head burst upon him, as he sat
at dinner with his family, he bade his wife look after
her, and hurried up to the Convent to let the frightened Nuns know where their patient might be found.
The Superior's carriage, fat horses and coachman,
with the stately lady herself inside, were soon seen
standing at Mr. Cutler's front door. Some passers-
by must have witnessed the struggle that ensued,
when poor Sister Mary John, screaming and raving
in delirium, was half forced, half persuaded, to enter
the carriage, which immediately returned to the Convent at a pace which probably astonished the fat
horses even more than the passers-by. In a few

2

hours an ingenious story began to be circulated in
and about Boston, and implicitly believed by many
people, to the following effect : "A poor Nun, who had
fallen under the displeasure of the tyrannical Superior,
and had been imprisoned a long time in the underground cells of the Convent, had at last contrived to
make her escape, but had been followed by the Superior to the house where she had taken refuge, and
carried back to the Convent by force, spite of her
cries and frantic resistance." A perfect storm of indignation followed the circulation of this story, which
it was almost impossible to refute, truth and falsehood were so mixed up in it. The indignation grew
and deepened unavoidably, for this story, of which
some of the facts were true, and all the inferences
false, seemed to justify the dislike and suspicion that
had long been gathering against the Convent. The
handsome building itself, overlooking the Sovereign
People's highway, and standing in extensive grounds
that must not be entered, invited the curiosity that it
repelled. So did the stranger ladies, the Nuns, who
occupied it, and who so entirely ignored the world
around them. In fact, the whole establishment was
as foreign to the soil whereon it stood as if, like Alad-
din's Palace, it had been wafted from Europe by the
power of a magician. During the winter before my
acquaintance with the Convent, occurred the great
revival of religion in New England, and the old

hatred of Catholicism woke up under its influence. As I mentioned before, Dr. Lyman Beecher delivered a course of lectures in Boston, in which the "Devil and the Pope of Rome" were never introduced one without the other, as inseparable in his mind as the Siamese Twins in body, — who, by the way, were first exhibited about that time. Dr. Beecher fiercely denounced convents, and enlightened the people as to the depravity popularly supposed to exist inside their walls. Very opportunely for the effect he wished to produce, a book called "Six Months in a Convent" was just then published, the work of a silly, ignorant, deceitful girl, a native of Charlestown, whom the Superior of the Ursuline Convent had charitably taken into her employ as a seamstress. The public mind was in exactly the condition to accept this book as true, and read it with avidity, though it was palpably a tissue of falsehoods and stupid misconceptions from end to end. It purported to relate the threats and persuasions used by the inmates of the Convent to make the writer a Catholic against her will, and it ended with an account of her escape from their clutches just in time to save herself from being carried off by force to St. Louis. The story proceeded in the usual melodramatic course, if I remember it rightly, — I am sure I have read it over again, under different titles, several times since! The girl — I can't remember her name — left an interesting orphan, excites the sympathy of good Catholics in the neighborhood of the Convent, by expressing an interest in their form of worship, and a dissatisfaction with her own Protestant creed, whatever it was, — " Methodist, Baptist, Hunker, Dunker, Shaker, or Quaker," as Southey says. The Superior of the Ursulines is persuaded to admit her into the Convent, that she may be taught the doctrines of the Church, and confirmed in her desire to embrace them. No doubt she was an important person among the Catholics at that time, and treated with attention, as converts were not so common as they are now. But after she enters the Convent, she finds that she has to work hard, to live abstemiously, to keep fasts, to perform penances, to rise early, to obey in silence, to have no will of her own, to live within four walls. She relates all these details of a conventual life, as if they were so many affronts put upon her by the Superior to punish her for changing her mind, while that lady's persuasive flatteries were by no means a sufficient counterbalance, — layers of *jam* too thin to cover such large pills. Catholicism lost all its charms for this young woman; her experience in the Convent dispelled all her romantic illusions in its favor; and the life of a Religieuse, on a near view, seemed beautiful no longer. She finds herself more of a Protestant than ever, and wonders how she ever came to desire to change her religion. Plenty of weeping and repentance through the book, till the young woman discovers the deep-laid plot to convey her to St. Louis for the purpose of shutting her up in a Convent there, and making a Catholic of her *by force.* *How* this is to be done is left a mystery over which the victim and her readers shudder together. Sleepless nights and agonized days follow this fearful discovery, but when, opportunely hidden behind the organ in the chapel, she overhears the Superior and Bishop Fenwick actually settling on the very day when this plot is to be carried out, the young woman can bear it no longer, but makes an elaborate escape from the Convent by climbing fences and breaking down lattice-work, to the best of my remembrance, in preference to walking out of the door, which could not have taken her half the time.

The indignant Protestants, who implicitly believed this false and foolish book, never asked themselves what motive but a charitable one could have induced the Superior to burden herself with the charge of a sickly, ignorant, poor, and friendless girl, who begged for her protection; and what motive she could have had for keeping such a useless creature *against her will.*

While "Six Months in a Convent" excited the lower classes of Boston and its vicinity against the Charlestown Nunnery, Mrs. Sherwood's "Nun," a fascinating tale which appeared about that time, prejudiced more intelligent people, who could not forbear mentally associating the only Convent they knew about with those of which they were reading in her book.

The Boston truckmen were at that time a well-organized body of men, — a sort of guild, who marched in Fourth of July processions, attired in white smock-frocks, and were cheered by the crowd for their manly bearing. They were of the same social status as the romancing authoress of " Six Months," and they took up her cause warmly, finding her story fully confirmed, as they honestly thought, by the escape and recapture of Sister Mary John, which the newspapers detailed at length in its perverted form. Secret indignation-meetings were being held by the truckmen and others, about the time when I entered the Ursuline Convent, and many persons supposed an attack on the Convent to be impending. Hence the visits, so mysterious to me, which my father received from certain friends who believed that danger threatened the Convent, and that it would be wise to delay my entrance into the Ursuline School. But he, and many other sensible people too, thought it impossible that any danger was to be apprehended as to a school composed almost entirely of Protestant pupils.

I am sorry to have interrupted my story by such a long digression, but while you read it you must imagine me jogging along to school in my father's chaise with a heavy heart, in spite of my new pink gingham frock *in esse*, and a consciousness of half a dozen more both pink and white *in posse*.

My recollections of the fortnight passed at the Ursuline School are fragmentary, but vivid; like scenes in a theatre, with the curtain of forgetfulness dropping between them. I remember arriving at the Convent late in the afternoon, just at the recreation hour, and I soon find myself gravely walking up and down one of the long terraces in the garden, already a Senior, — greatly to my sorrow, and obliged to behave with a Senior's dignity, while the happy little Juniors were skipping and playing in the walk above. I owed the misfortune of being made a member of the Senior class to the advanced state of my studies, which fact, considering the low standard of education at that time in girls' schools, I may mention without vanity. There were several children about my age in the Senior class, but most of the girls were older, and I felt miserably out of place in their company, especially as I had been brought up with children younger than myself. Most of the Seniors had already passed through the Junior class, and were old acquaintances, having a free-and-easy way with each other that I was sure I never, *never* should acquire. Apropos of this feeling, I remember that the girl whose desk was next to mine in the

school-room kept concealed therein a certain mysterious treasure, namely, a fragment of broken look-
ing-glass, at which intimate friends were allowed
sometimes to peep; there were no mirrors in our
dormitories, which made this an inestimable privilege, and I was so overcome one day by the apprehension that I should *never, never* become one
of those favored friends — not even if I remained at
school till I was twenty years old, as my father had
decreed — that I burst suddenly into tears, and was
fain to hide my head behind my desk-cover. Of
course this foolish feeling was only one of the miserable symptoms of homesickness.

On this first afternoon of my school experience on
the Senior walk, I met the scrutinizing glances bestowed by my companions on me as a new scholar,
with deep blushes and deprecating smiles, feeling
very awkward in my solitude, while they were prom-
enading up and down, each with her " particular
friend," enjoying the luxury of whispering secrets
in each other's ears. I began to meditate how I
could best climb the bank and reach the Juniors in
their walk above me, with whom I longed to play,
for *they* had dolls, so much better than " particular
friends," and some of them were nursing their dolls
with an air of maternal solicitude which quite won my
heart. I was sure I should easily get acquainted with
such anxious mammas, for we should meet on com-

mon ground, — surely they could sympathize in my grief at parting with Claribel, and my reminiscences of that darling must interest them deeply.

Imagine my mortification when, just as I had climbed to the top of the bank, a severe voice from below called out, "Miss Goddard, come down at once!" I turned, hardly knowing myself under this new title of *Miss*, and saw one of the black-robed sisters beckoning with her finger to hurry my movements. Several Juniors had stopped their play and come up to look at me, and I had to make my ignominious descent before their curious eyes. Unluckily I slipped, and rolled sprawling down the bank, with my legs and arms rotating like the spokes of a broken wheel; the Juniors laughed aloud and my face burned like fire.

The black Nun did not laugh; however, she looked at me very gravely as she told me it was against the rules for Seniors and Juniors to hold any communication with each other except by special permission, but, as I was a new scholar, she would not report me for misdemeanor this time, only I was to beware for the future. So saying, she moved slowly away in her heavy black robes, which must have been oppressively warm on that summer day. But the Nuns always looked cool and comfortable, and I used to wonder how it was that they never *perspired!* — at least I never saw any sign of perspiration on their muffled faces.

Quite humbled in spirit, I retired to a distance from the place of my downfall, and seated myself under a smoke-bush. A Senior I was, and a Senior unmixed I must remain, so it appeared, and as a Senior and Miss Goddard into the bargain, I ought not to cry; but I could not help shedding a few tears, which I wiped away hurriedly on hearing footsteps approaching. Another pair of "particular friends" who had strolled to the farther end of the walk appeared returning, with arms intertwined, and so deep in confidential talk that they did not notice me, the poor little Solitary. But as they passed me I recognized in one of them an old schoolmate of mine, Mary H——; old schoolmate indeed! at this moment, amid the novelty of my surroundings, it seemed to me that I must have known her in another sphere of existence. I jumped up from my low seat and called her by name; she stopped abruptly, looked at me and knew me at once. I can't say she seemed overjoyed to see me, nor, indeed, should I have been specially glad to meet her anywhere else but in this place where I felt so lonely. "Why, Louisa Goddard, how did *you* come here?" was her first, not very flattering question. "I did n't know *you* were to be one of the new scholars. Just got here? Wonder how you 'll like it? Darling Bella," turning to her friend, who had politely withdrawn to the opposite side of the alley, "wait for me a moment.

I 'll join you directly." " No hurry," returned that young lady, taking the opportunity to empty her shoes of gravel by leaning against a syringa-bush, and standing on one leg at a time. Mary and I looked at each other silently for a minute. We had formerly been rivals at a little school kept by a certain Miss J——, a girl only sixteen years old, who was extremely proud of us " advanced pupils " amid a little crowd of A B C-darians. We were eight or nine years old, and we two composed the " first class," and recited together out of Wood-bridge's Geography, Colburn's " First Lessons," and Murray's " Abridged."

Miss J——, with great want of judgment, used to stimulate us to exertion in study, by pitting us against each other, making constant comparisons between us, and praising each of us alternately, at the other's expense, so that we generally disliked one another cordially. Sometimes, however, when the pursuit of knowledge presented unusual difficulties, we sympathized mutually, — as when Miss J—— gave us passages to parse from " Paradise Lost," where Milton shows his grammatical genius in separating his nominative cases from his verbs by immense distances. Till we became shrewd enough to look for the nominative in the first line, and the verb in the last line of these passages, and pay no attention to the rest of them, we were often hopelessly

puzzled, and quite disposed to help each other by
" prompting." Miss J—— used to make us " parse "
from opposite corners of the room, puss-in-the-corner
fashion, in order to prevent it. And in " recess " we
sometimes fell back into friendship, when, I am sorry
to say, we too often encouraged each other in being
naughty and ungovernable, taking pleasure in putting
our foolish young teacher to her wit's end for means
to control us.

As Mary and I stood looking at each other, the
memory of those half-forgotten days came back to
us both, and, being now at the mature age of eleven
or twelve, we had the grace to feel ashamed of our
youthful follies. " Louisa," said Mary, coming close
to my ear, " we were really very naughty girls at
Miss J——'s school sometimes. I can tell you I
behave very differently now, and so I hope do *you*,"
which she said with a patronizing air that recalled
all my old dislike. " Now we will promise never to
tell of each other here, and while we are at the Convent we must not talk before the girls about Miss
J——'s school, or let them know we ever went there
together." Having made this abrupt and sensible
proposition, to which " *of course* I said *yes*," —like Fair
Zurich's daughter, in the popular song of that day, —
Mary returned to darling Bella, leaving me *plantée*
under the smoke-bush and more discontented than
ever, as there I sat in melancholy mood, watching

the girls' pink frocks moving about in the rays of
the sinking sun.

In this way began my fortnight's experience in the
Ursuline Convent, which made a deep and lasting
impression on me because of its strangeness. School
life in a foreign convent, French or Belgian, would
have been no stranger, save that we should have
spoken French. Never to be alone, always to be
under supervision, — these novel conditions made me
unutterably melancholy. I will try and recall the
routine that we followed day after day. There were
no *rooms* in that part of the building devoted to the
pupils, — rooms are for a few, *halls* for many, — and
we inhabited halls exclusively. Each dormitory was
occupied by sixteen girls; there were eight windows
on each side, and room for a little white bed between
every two, while small washstands stood under each
window. The floor was carpetless, the windows cur-
tainless, — each girl's trunk was placed at the foot
of her bed. There were two windows at the end of
the dormitory, and it was considered a great privilege
to be allowed to occupy the beds next them; it was
comparative privacy to have a neighbor only on one
side, and comparative freedom to have a double out-
look upon the world. Very early in the morning the
great dormitory was thrown open, and Sister Mary
Austin, our special guardian, appeared on the threshold, when she crossed herself devoutly, and began to

recite " Matins " aloud, as she slowly walked along
the aisle between the rows of beds. This she did
with as much dignity as was compatible with her
duty of waking up the girls, by dragging the bedclothes off them to the right and left as she proceeded,
practice having given her great skill in suddenly ex-
posing the attitudes of the sleepers. I used to sit up
and watch them; some with knees touching their
chins, some in a huddle, some on their backs, with
arms at right angles, or tossed over their heads, and
some in statuesque positions, with folded hands and
feet crossed. There was only one moment of immobil-
ity, and then every girl was out of bed, dressing
and washing silently. Then in procession we went
through the broad halls, first to the school-room,
where we knelt down in a double row, each girl
before her desk, while one of the oldest pupils,
kneeling alone at the head of the room, read or recited, according as she was Protestant or Catholic,
the morning prayers of the Catholic church. The
school-room was a very large one, — Seniors from
other dormitories joined in the exercise, — and I
amused myself by noticing which girls crossed themselves during prayers, and must therefore be Catholics. They were few in number, and generally
foreign-looking. Then came the procession to the
Refectory, where some elderly lay-sisters waited on
the long tables which were set out with the regulation

spoons and mugs, and not much else. Melancholy
as was my usual state of mind during that fortnight,
I felt a new access of misery whenever meal-times
arrived. Dry bread, though excellent of its kind,
and a mugful of milk for breakfast; dry bread and
a bit of butter, with a glass of water for supper, —
meagre as this food seemed to me, I thought I could
have swallowed it philosophically had I been able
to look forward and backward upon a good dinner.
We usually had but one course at this meal, soup
made with vegetables one day, soup-meat mixed with
vegetables on the next. Salt-fish ditto, or hasty-
pudding and molasses, or rice-milk on Fridays and
fast-days, which seemed to me to be very frequent
at that time. Having spent my early childhood
in an English nursery, I had as great a hatred
of rice-pudding as little Reginald in Charles Reade's
story. "There filthy there abbommanabel," as he
said, and I thought. I always wept into my mug of
water till it was salt on rice-milk days. Sometimes
for a treat we had each three or four dried and flat-
tened prunes or figs, wizened to the size of beans,
served in little cup-plates. Even our young teeth
could hardly gnaw them, and the girls declared them
to be bits of the Sisters' old shoes, chopped up with
a hatchet. Even that exquisite joke failed to make
me laugh in my disgust. I confess I did not get
much sympathy in my misery, for the pupils, accus-

tomed to the diet, cheerfully swallowed what was set
before them and thought no more about it, save occasionally to remind each other of the feast-days that
were to come, particularly " Coronation day " and
church-festivals, when the girls were put in good
humor with Catholicism by little entertainments got
up in real French taste. I can only say that there
are no fête-days of the church in the later summer,
so far as my Convent experience goes.

However, we had food for our souls if not for our
bodies at meal-times ; the older girls read aloud from
the head of the different tables the Lives of the Saints.
Protestant children were not expected to listen unless
they chose, — one of the liberal practices in the Convent which raised the school into high favor with
their parents. These " Lives " were quite as interesting to me as fairy stories, — and much like them,
— and, having nothing to do in the way of eat-
ing, I listened with all my ears. Our light meals
were accompanied by " Grace before and after Meat,"
peculiarly long, and there was much bending and
crossing among the Catholic pupils, who really worked
very hard in keeping up the piety of the institution,
while the Protestants looked on idly. I used to say
to myself, indignantly, " It is a shame that the less
we receive the more thankful we have to be."

After breakfast the processions moved back to their
several school-rooms, and half an hour's recreation

was allowed, or rather the privilege of using the tongue for half an hour; there were no playthings or games, only a babel of voices was heard. Then followed some hours of silence, when the girls were supposed to be studying, and Sister Mary Austin held the books while the classes stumbled through or gabbled over their lessons. I don't remember that she ever explained a passage or talked with them about their tasks; she used to take out her handkerchief and yawn behind it very often. Then came more processions to and from the noon dinner, and short recreation in the school-rooms before and after that meal. In the afternoon, hours of silence; fancy-work was pursued zealously by the girls; some of them had seemed half asleep over the morning lessons, but they waked up thoroughly over their canvas and crewels, velvets and paints, and even Sister Mary Austin yawned no more. I had no fancy-work, only some dreadful plain sewing, — some under-garments that my mother had given me to make, and which Sister Mary Austin basted for me under protest. These cotton seams sunk me greatly in my own esteem and increased my melancholy. For some reason that I have forgotten, I studied very little during my stay at the Convent and was put into no class. I used to sit and long impatiently for the time when Sister Mary Austin would place me, perhaps, in the first class, where I should astonish the

3

big girls by my brilliant recitations, and compel their
respect in spite of my plain sewing.

Late in the afternoon we walked in procession for
our sun-bonnets, hanging in a back hall, put them
on as nearly simultaneously as possible, and then
two by two made our way into that part of the
grounds known as the Bowers, — two broad grassy
avenues, having between them something that was
neither a hedge nor a thicket; a deep tangled wall
of greenery in whose recesses a double row of leafy
arbors had been made. These were the summer
playing-places of the pupils, Seniors and Juniors
occupying different rows on opposite sides of the
green partition, and being strictly forbidden to hold
any intercourse with each other. But the happy
Juniors played with all their might, and I, having
neither bosom friend nor fancy-work, used to sit on
the grass and watch their energetic housekeeping,
a family in every arbor, dolls lolling about against
the branches, and tea-tables arranged on low stumps.
A dear aged Sister in spectacles, who darned stockings continually, had charge of the Juniors, and was
even good-natured enough to let them pull at her
rosary as an imaginary bell, and to sit quite still
while a sick doll was carefully put to bed on her
shoulder and covered with her veil. I witnessed
many small breaches of discipline, — whisperings
between Seniors and Juniors, Pyramus and Thisbe

fashion, candy given and received, and notes hastily
passed, scribbled on the fly-leaves of school-books.
Unhappy child that I was! a prisoner and nothing
to do. The Convent cows, unwatched and grazing
freely over a large pasture, filled me with envy; I
longed to be a cow or a bird or a spider or an ant, —
any one of the happy creatures at liberty around me.
In fact, I was a doll-less child for the first time in my
life, — which is quite as bad as being a dogless man,
— and I actually mourned for my waxen Claribel as
Rachel mourneth for her children. Had I only been
a Junior, I could, I thought, in some way purchase
a right of adoption in some one of their darlings.

After tea there was another hour of profound silence enjoined while the Nuns were at the Vesper
service. My soul thrills as I recall the melancholy
beauty of that hour. Motionless, I watched the slow
setting of the sun, lighting up the broad summer
landscape with a golden glow and darkening it
with purple shadows; and when the sun had dropped
behind the distant hills, and the changing opal sky
was fading into dull gray, the voices of the Sisters
rose solemnly from the Chapel below, and the faint
scent of incense mingled with the breath of the white
roses trained against its walls, and floated into the
open window on the evening air.

The Convent, with its broad halls, long galleries,
and massive walls, put me in mind of palaces about

which I had read. The great music-room with its
piano, the handsome gilt harp and guitars dressed in
uniforms of pink ribbons, seemed to me elegant enough
to be used for a meeting of Troubadours. I took
several music-lessons there of Sister Mary John, the
unfortunate Mother-Assistant, who showed, by her
nervous, excitable manner and flushed face, that she
had not yet recovered entirely from that terrible
brain-fever.

How I enjoyed the little moments of transit between the school-room and music-room as I went to
my lessons and returned from them! for they were
my only periods of solitude and freedom from supervision, — I used to linger on the stairs, jump up and
down them three at a time, dance wildly, and even
make faces by way of making the most of my liberty,
— and I felt an ever-growing desire to take advantage
of it for the gratification of my curiosity. The pupils
were positively forbidden to visit any part of the
building save the halls appropriated to their use ; and
few, even of those who had been at the school for
years, had ever attempted to break this rule. Yet
legends of adventurous spirits were handed down
from year to year, and circulated among the new girls,
and I had overheard just enough to excite my imagination. " Such and such girls had made their way
— oh ! — as far as — um — um — um — (whispering) — and seen — O gracious, they had seen the

strangest things, for instance, um — um — um — (whispers again) and had heard — O, they were so frightened ! — such tones — um — um — strange voices — um — um — cries, — groans, — sobs — " (tragic whispers, shuddering, expressive silence). There was a brick tomb, a very large one, at the bottom of the garden, where certain Nuns were buried, and about which the girls made many surmises, which in time grew into dreadful stories, told to new-comers with bated breath.

On my way to the music-room I had to pass the foot of the stairs leading to the upper stories of the Convent, which were supposed to be as much out of our reach as heaven itself. We were forbidden to go there ; and, according to school-girl logic, that was sufficient proof that wickedness was enacted there, in Chambers of Horrors. I do believe these ridiculous fancies, held by Protestant children to account for a novel discipline which they could not comprehend, obtained circulation among certain classes outside the Convent, and assisted in bringing on the catastrophe which destroyed the school.

When I first crossed the foot of those stairs I looked up with straining eyes, and wondered what I should see if I had ever the courage to mount them. On the next occasion I began to think I might find the courage, and on the conclusion of my second lesson, when I was to pass those stairs for the fourth time, I suddenly resolved to venture then and there, and, clasping my hands tightly together over my heart, which beat so furiously that I could hardly breathe, I flew rather than ran up to the first landing, but beyond that point I dared not go. However, I saw quite enough to give my excited imagination a rude shock, and to bring common-sense to the front. The stairs ended in another broad hall, with sundry dormitories opening upon it, through whose half-open doors I could see rows of little white beds just like our own. Even in that moment I was impressed with the exquisite neatness that prevailed, and the spotless purity of the carpetless floors; for, as in all foreign convents, the floors were made of hard wood or solid stone, and were uncovered. Dead silence reigned, and solitude, for the inhabitants of that upper story were all busy in their various duties below. Small pictures in black frames and crucifixes hung on the white walls above the bed-heads; no other furniture was visible; a clock ticked loudly in the silence, and seemed to address me personally with a stern " Go away, go away, go away ! " And down stairs again I flew, well rewarded for my temerity, had I been old enough to know it, by the wholesome disbelief that I began to feel, after this experience, in the abominable stories whispered about among the girls, partly because their lives of unnatural seclusion gave them little else to talk about and deprived them of any other excitement.

In our various processions through the main hall
of the building, we always passed the great double
doors of the Chapel, which opened upon it. Sometimes those doors would be ajar, giving us a glimpse
of the interior, where some one of the Catholic pupils
was often seen kneeling in penance. A Canadian
girl named Susanne P——— was frequently punished
in this manner for giving way to sudden outbursts
of angry violence, without apparent reason save that
she had an unusual quantity of *red hair*. This was
supposed to be the infallible accompaniment of *a
temper*, and indeed might well be the cause of it,
as in those days the owner of red hair was alternately snubbed and ridiculed for that misfortune
by her brown-haired and black-haired companions.
"Red Hair," this was the name given by unappreciative
school-girls to Susanne's magnificent locks, by which
even I, ignorant little thing as I was, well remember
her. She had large black eyes, which, by contrast
with her hair, added to the singularity of her appearance. These eyes she was accustomed during school-
hours to fix on vacancy, wherever that may be, while
she would clasp round her knees a pair of very white
hands spotted with freckles, which were, as I noticed,
just the color of her hair. She would forget the book
she was studying, and let it slip gradually off her
knee till it fell to the floor with a loud bang, which
often made Sister Mary Austin jump in the middle

of a yawn, and drew upon Susanne the attention of
the whole school. She was a silent, reserved girl,
except when she fell into one of her sudden passions,
and on such occasions she had a way of hiding herself behind the waves of her bright hair, which had
an electric sparkle and vitality singularly in contrast
with her pale still face. Every hair seemed instinct
with separate life, and her great eyes fairly caught
a dull glow from the influence of this superb *cheve-
lure.* I could not forbear looking at her compassionately when I saw her so often in the Chapel kneeling
motionless as marble under this living hair; and,
lowly as her head was bent, I thought I could de-
tect a glance of recognition sliding from under her
eyelids.

Sundays we all attended High Mass in the Chapel,
the Protestant girls taking their Bibles with them,
which they were supposed by their parents to read
diligently during the services. I am sorry to say
the only diligent readers I saw were those who had
contrived to conceal story-books between the covers.
A low partition separated us from the main body
of the Chapel, and behind a similar partition on
the opposite side was the apartment occupied by
the Nuns during Mass. Heavy crimson curtains,
slightly parted, effectually concealed them, filling up
most of the space above the partition. But, though
unseen, their exquisite singing ravished the ear, so

ravished my childish senses that I should not have been surprised had a troop of angels swooped out upon us from between the parted curtains, with white wings brushing the crimson, looking perhaps like the beautiful St. Ursula over the altar.

I was not old enough to appreciate the value of the solid silver candlesticks and vessels that furnished the altar, or the silver-gilt communion-service used by the Bishop at High Mass. The older girls had much to say on the subject, and they were never tired of admiring the elegance of the lace made by the Nuns for their Chapel, and the splendor of the Bishop's robes embroidered by them. But O, the pictures! Really valuable works by foreign artists hung on the walls, so utterly unlike any pictures I had ever seen that I could not look at them as such. The genius that had breathed a soul into them, such as a grown-up amateur would have appreciated as the perfection of art, informed them to *my* inexperienced eye with an almost real life and breath, that awed me inexpressibly. I remember one full-length figure of some virgin saint, with flowing robes and hair, and a face of perfect loveliness, glowing with ecstatic devotion, as her eyes, piercing heaven for " ten thousand perpendicular miles," — such was my childish thought, — seemed to hold in their gaze a *something* not even to be guessed at. While I was losing myself in this picture,

I wondered how the girls about me could fidget, and sigh, and complain in whispers of the discomfort of their kneeling positions. Where else *could* one be but on one's knees in presence of that picture? was my feeling. I remember specially only one more painting, probably because it was so complete a contrast to the other. It was the head of an aged ascetic dying in the wilderness, starved to skin and bone, with shrivelled arms and claw-like fingers, with which he hardly had strength to clasp a crucifix against his ragged robe. There was a skull in the picture, — much resembling the lean head of the Monk, — crossbones, a great book, and the mouth of a cave. *His* eyes, too, were raised upward, but " O dear," thought I, " he only wants the Lord to see the red rings about them, and their livid sockets." These pictured saints seemed to my imagination endowed with a mysterious life of their own, and I always fancied the chapel inhabited by their moving figures when the doors were shut and locked, as they often were when we passed by in procession.

There was a great difference in the behavior of the Protestant and Catholic girls at chapel. Many of the former made it their business to assume indifference to the services, for which reason, perhaps, the few Catholics felt called upon to show a more than usual devotion thereat. A beautiful Creole girl, the oldest of the Catholic pupils, set them a perfect example in that respect. I suppose I noticed her particularly on account of the contrast she presented to Susanne P——, who was her neighbor at Sunday morning Mass, — for the Catholic girls liked to be together, — kneeling so close to her side that her bright locks touched the lovely Creole's dusky cheek and her bands of ebon hair. But Susanne's eyes, with their sparks of fire, were often fixed in upward glance, while Louisa Murdock — that was the name of the West-Indian beauty — kept hers hidden under their black lashes.

I began to know the names of those girls who most interested me. Ellen and Rosamond Moriarty were Catholics, sisters ; Ellen rosy, laughing, brilliant in health and spirits, and poor Rosamond sullen, pitted with small-pox, with a harelip and no palate, so that her imperfect discordant speech was a foil to her sister's joyous sweetness of voice. There were four sisters named Williams, — two in the Senior and two in the Junior class, — four sizes of pink frocks, and all the wearers pretty. The oldest was handsome, and was beginning to know it and to look forward to leaving school and wearing something better than a pink frock. The second was a grave, quiet girl, a great favorite with the Nuns, as she already showed a strong leaning to a conventual life, and indeed she did at last become both a Catholic and an Ursuline nun. The younger ones, unless by special permission, only saw their sisters to speak with them on dancing days, when

Elizabeth settled their sashes, and Penelope gave them good advice ; for on that day the classes were taught together. Nearly all dressed in white frocks, and a holiday feeling pervaded the school. A certain Penelope English was one of the prettiest dancers ; she *chasséed* about merrily, with a smile for every one she met. She was the motherless daughter of an officer, and had lost the use of one eye, which was always covered by a green shade. But the other was of a lovely laughing violet-blue, and its glance, when it met yours, so pleasant that it was worth that of any two eyes in the whole school. One little girl wore a superb net, with heavy tassels, all of blue saddler's silk. "Too lovely for anything," I thought both her and her net, and I wished I could conceal my mop of hair under such an elegant appendage. I was somewhat ashamed of it, as it had lately been cut by our maiden aunt, who was in the habit of bringing her shears twice a year into our family, and "barbering" us in an eccentric fashion of her own, the heads of both boys and girls looking exactly alike when they came from under her hands. She was kind enough to pay us a flying visit when she heard I was about to be sent to school, in order to give my hair an extra touch, and she pronounced her work a triumph of art, when finished. My head was indeed "a unique," as I saw, after comparing it with the heads of my schoolmates, not so fortunate as myself in maiden aunts with a genius for men's business. I should add, to do her justice, that she could "carpenter," paper-hang and paint, and once "marbled" her front staircase so handsomely that it saved her the purchase of a carpet.

The little girl with the blue silk net was called Anna Augusta; such an appropriate name, I thought, for the owner of that exquisite thing. I resolved that if ever Claribel had a sister, she should be christened Anna Augusta.

One lovely girl among the pupils, named Maria F——, had the face of a young Madonna, with a sweet, pure, *still* expression, that made it a pleasure for me to look upon her, she seemed so peculiarly fit to be in a convent. Some of the wild, turbulent children seemed entirely out of place in a community of nuns, while Maria's looks and ways were in perfect harmony with her surroundings; she might have been the youngest of St. Ursula's ten thousand virgins. Mary B——, a complete contrast to the placid Maria in manners, was the wit of the Senior class. She was as given to graceful gestures as a French girl, her pantomime was as expressive as her words; we always opened our mouths, prepared to laugh, whenever she opened hers to speak, — even I, the melancholy Jacqueline of the class.

After Mass, on my first Sunday at the Convent, the Superior sent for me to come to her own room, whither I was escorted by a Sister, who knocked for

me on the door. She was graciously invited to
enter with me, which she did, bending her body rever-
ently. I suppose this honor was conferred on me by
way of curing my homesickness, of which the Superior had been told. She was very gracious to me,
presenting me to the Bishop, who had just officiated
at Mass, and who, without his brocade robes stiff with
embroidery, looked to me like a peacock stripped of
his feathers. I am afraid my miserable discontent
made me very sarcastic; soon, though, I was desperately frightened at finding myself in the Presence.
The Superior was a very portly woman, even stout,
but I believe I have mentioned that she carried herself with royal dignity, and even arrogance. The
whole household feared her; she spoke sharply to the
Nuns, who bowed before her; the servants always
approached her with bent head, downcast eyes, and
hands crossed on their breasts. The pupils were taught
to rise simultaneously whenever she entered any one
of the school-rooms, and to remain standing while
she swept through it, and as long as she continued to
occupy the seat prepared for her at the head of the
room, which she filled as if it had been a throne.
With the Bishop alone was she on equal terms, and
when, on this my visit to her apartment, my fright
allowed me the use of my senses, it seemed to me
they were sitting together just like any old lady and
gentleman, only that they appeared very happy in

wrangling and contradicting each other,— poor things! except when together they never could enjoy the pleasure of disputing, for they were despotic sovereigns elsewhere, and nobody dared oppose them. Each carried a silver-gilt snuff-box, which they presented one to the other at intervals, taking friendly pinches of snuff together when controversy lulled. There was a pause after I had been introduced to the Bishop as a new pupil, and had placed myself at his knee, by the Superior's order. " This little girl is ridiculously homesick ; what shall we do with her ? " said she in an admonitory tone, and looking at the Bishop as if expecting him to lecture me on my folly. I dared not lift my eyes to his face, and in the silence that followed, the ticking of the mantel clock and the beating of my heart seemed to be racing with each other. At length the Bishop spoke, and sharply. " Take your fingers out of your mouth," said he, " and go to Sister Mary Francis, and ask her to tie up your frock." Relieved, but ashamed, I crept up to the Nun who had brought me to the Superior's room ; she hastened to obey the command, and drew the string so tightly that it broke, and I was allowed to make my escape in her company. My unfortunate sloping shoulders, which were always letting my frocks drop out of place, and getting me into trouble, for once did me a good turn. I was even glad to get back to my Sunday lesson, the " getting by heart," as the phrase

goes, of a chapter in the Testament. Poor Sister
Mary Austin found Sunday anything but a holiday,
for it was her duty to "hear" every girl in the Senior
class recite a chapter; her religious opinions, I suppose, were considered to be so firmly fixed as to be
proof against the influence of the heretical Bible.
Indeed, as the girls hesitated, stumbled, or drawled
through their recitations while she prompted or
reproved or waited or yawned, I thought she must
get such a surfeit of our Bible as fairly to dislike it.
I used to wonder at the constancy of Sister Mary
Austin's yawns, till I heard the girls alluding to mid-
night masses, four o'clock matins, and mysterious
penances practised at night.

Once, and only once during that homesick fortnight
at the Convent, I laughed aloud, and it happened in
this wise. As in melancholy mood I was sitting on
the grass during afternoon recreation in the garden,
gazing vaguely towards the Convent, I suddenly
spied, outside an upper window, a black object that
hung suspended between heaven and earth. I walked
towards it, and it resolved itself into Sister Mary
Bernard cleaning the window on the *outside*. She
was a lay Sister, a servant who had taken the vows;
there were several of them. There she was, outside
on a buck-board, with her feet in old shoes down at
the heel, pointing toward heaven, and a great length
of black worsted stocking visib'e, embroidered with

darns and openworked with holes. Her rusty black veil streamed out behind in the breeze, like a banner wildly waving; her white forehead-band was dragged disreputably over one eye; and her rosary went bump, bump against the buck-board as she energetically brandished a towel aloft.

I remember but little about the Nuns; a few of their names I picked up, but to my unaccustomed eye they all looked alike. There was but one novice in a white veil, whom we pitied profoundly, for she was in the last stages of consumption, her face as white as her veil, and her hollow cough echoed about the house. She was young, pretty, and so anxious to mortify her poor dying flesh that she persisted in fulfilling her duties to the utmost limit of her strength, and I have often seen her totter and catch hold of the table to support herself, as she waited on the little ones in the refectory.

And now a ray, or rather a whole sun, of joy lighted up my unhappy life, to my great astonishment. By the rules of the school the pupils were allowed to go home and spend Sunday once a month; therefore to the end of my first month at school I was looking forward with inexpressible longing. The first fortnight had dragged itself away, and I was beginning to count the days of the second, with the feeling of one who has clambered with difficulty to the top of a hill, and prepares hopefully to run down to the bottom

4

again, knowing that the distance, though the same, will seem shorter as one's steps are accelerated. I had received no visit from home during the whole long fortnight, which made me sad, as other girls were daily sent for to see their friends. My heart used to beat fast with hope when the servant whose business it was to summon pupils to the parlor appeared at the school-room door, and then sink with disappointment when another name than mine was called. But quite early one Saturday morning my turn came, and " Miss Louisa Goddard " was asked for. How musically Bridget's brogue sounded in pronouncing my name! I was so dizzy with delight that I could hardly walk out of the school-room, and the girls nodded and looked at me kindly as I passed the rows of desks. Indeed, had my stay in the Convent been prolonged, I should of course have recovered from homesickness, made friends with the girls of my class, and been very happy. On this Saturday I certainly was so, for my father, whom I found in the parlor, told me that, notwithstanding the rule of the school, the Superior had given him permission to take me home to spend Sunday. I suppose he had had a conference with Sister Mary Benedict, the lovely Nun whose business it was to fascinate visitors, and the ruling powers had decided that an early visit home would assuage my homesickness, I being an unusual sufferer from that disease. I know I was very grateful to the Superior for the permission, as I flew up stairs through the solitary halls and dressed in the empty dormitory.

What happy days were the Saturday and Sunday I passed at home! With what absorbed attention my little brothers and sisters, from ten years old to two, listened to my school experiences, ranged about me as I sat on the pump-platform in the garden, — a flight of short steps of which I was the top-stair. With what solicitude I nursed and fed my doll, waking her from her fortnight's nap, and how pleased I was when my black rabbit, to whom I made an immediate visit, loped up in a friendly way, and wiggled his nose up and down against my hand. A body-guard of children escorted me to the stable, — the summer baby-house, which was under a convenient pile of planks, for the benefit of the dolls' health, who were then supposed to be boarding in the country, — and to the purple-plum tree, where I was made to sit down, while my sister Lucretia tore her pinafore in climbing up to the most eligible *shaking place.* My mother tried to talk to me about my clothes, and my father about my studies, but I am afraid I did not pay much attention to their words of wisdom. Monday morning came only too soon; it seemed impossible I should have been at home two days, and I felt that when I returned to the Convent my visit would only appear like one of those vivid dreams of home that were at once my solace and my misery. I assured my mother of this, with tears rolling down my cheeks, and I begged her at least to let me take my doll back with me, as a proof that I had been awake. I told her I was not a bit ashamed to be the only girl in the Senior class who played with a doll; and she at last consented. Then I vowed to my dear Claribel to be so devoted to her that she should never suffer as I had from homesickness, even though she should have no companion in the Senior class, and should be forbidden by the rules to get acquainted with any doll in the Junior class, however desirable. My sister Anne generously lent me a small trunk in which to pack Claribel's clothes, we both lamenting that there was no time to put her into uniform, and in return I gave Anne my buff kitten, in whose character, as she developed into cathood, I was in truth disappointed. In the most slovenly manner she had already dirtied and torn her whole month's wardrobe of ribbons, that I had so carefully prepared for her; and, worse still, she had caught a mouse, and showed a determination to catch more, — a thing for which in her early youth I had hoped she had a special antipathy.

On the whole, I made my second journey to school with a lighter heart than I bore in my bosom on the first, Claribel clasped in my arms, and my feet resting on her trunk as my father and I again drove from Dorchester to Charlestown in the chaise. He had

been strongly advised not to allow me to return, some
of his friends assuring him that the dislike and suspicion which had long been growing against the Convent had at last reached positive hatred, and that its
destruction was openly threatened. But my father
still laughed these apprehensions to scorn, and was
totally incredulous of danger to the Convent. I had
listened with great interest to these conversations between my father and his friends, and I quite understood them, for at school I had heard the older pupils
talking the matter over eagerly, and I was familiar
with the story of Sister Mary John's escape and recapture. I had besides "assisted" at various disputes
held among the girls about that notorious book, "Six
Months in a Convent," and the character of its author.
Sectarian spirit ran very high, — the Catholic girls
vehemently denouncing her, and declaring her book
to be one long falsehood, while a few bigoted Protestants were sure there was much to be said on her side.
Most of the pup' s were quite indifferent, however, to
the subject, save that they enjoyed the fun of listening
to the quarrel.

So on this my return journey to the Convent, I
was not surprised to find my father stopped on the
way by an old acquaintance, Mr. C——, whom we
met driving rapidly out of town on his way to our
house, his errand being to warn my father of the
certainty of danger to the Convent. When he passed

us, he made a sign to my father to halt, sprang out
of his vehicle, laid his hand on the reins, and was
almost ready to force my father to turn about, while
he rapidly and eagerly repeated to him facts that had
come to his knowledge respecting the designs of certain ill-conditioned persons on the Ursuline Convent.
I heard the word " mob " used by him several times,
and the assurance that the very Monday night just
approaching had been fixed upon by the " mob " for
the destruction of the " Nunnery," as they called it.
How I did hope my father would listen to Mr. C——
and turn back ! Not that the idea of a *mob* frightened
me, though I had read of the French Revolution, and
my mother had described the Bread Riots in England,
which she had herself witnessed; but it would be
so nice to go home again and surprise the children !
Still my father shook his head incredulously, declared
there was no possible danger to be feared for the Convent, and Mr. C—— left him very reluctantly, after
using some strong language of disapproval, at which
papa only laughed. So on we drove again, and I was
somewhat consoled for my disappointment in not returning home by feeling myself a sort of heroine.

And on reaching Mount Benedict I found the
whole school in commotion. Instead of silence and
emptiness in the halls, girls were actually passing
through them ; there was no studying in the Senior
school-room, but the older girls drew crowding round

Sister Mary Austin talking eagerly, while the younger
ones pressed close behind to listen, or followed their
own devices at their desks. I had expected to be
told to put my doll into my trunk till afternoon recreation, but no notice was taken of her, and I hastened to hide her in my desk, and put her trunk
underneath it. Alas, alas, dearest Claribel! little did
I think that I was looking on your face for the last
time, as I tenderly covered it with a bit of blotting-
paper, and hid it behind " Blair's Rhetoric." As
soon as these maternal duties were finished, I joined
the circle about Sister Mary Austin, and learned that
great events had happened in my absence. Floating
rumors of designs against the Convent had of course
reached the Nuns from time to time, but as the
Bishop disbelieved utterly in them, of course so did
these poor helpless women. But on the very Saturday which began my little holiday the Superior had
received formal notice that she was in danger, — she,
her community, and the building they occupied, —
from the Selectmen of Charlestown, and in a few hours
afterward they sent up a committee, chosen from their
number, to consult with the Superior as to what
should be done for her defence, and to ask permission
to examine the vaults of the building. They wished
to be able to contradict the report, generally believed,
that there were cells under the Convent, used for the
punishment of the refractory Nuns, and also secret

places of torment and iniquity. The Superior failed to appreciate the kind motives of these worthy Select-men ; she was furiously indignant at the abominable stories in circulation about her and her community, and when their committee were admitted to her presence, she overwhelmed them with a torrent of invectives, refused to allow them to examine her cellars, and if she had possessed the power, she would have scourged them from her gate. She appeared to hold them responsible for stories which they only repeated. But Sister Mary John, the Mother Assistant, received the deputation of Selectmen in a very different spirit. She considered herself the innocent cause of the reports that were blasting the reputation of the Convent, and perhaps bringing destruction upon it ; and she besought the Superior to allow her to explain the facts relative to her illness and its results, in presence of the committee. She did so with all her eloquence, and with such an air of truth that the gentlemen appeared to believe her entirely, and they promised to publish a card in Monday morning's papers, explaining the circumstances that had led to the story of the escaped Nun, recaptured and brought back to the cells of the underground Convent against her will, which, as they now believed, and as she assured them, had their origin in the circumstances of her illness.

On Monday morning this statement appeared in the papers, but coupled with an account of the reception given the committee of Charlestown Selectmen by the Superior of the Convent, and her refusal to allow them to examine the cellars of the building for themselves. She had received visits also from other gentlemen, — some dictated by friendship, others by curiosity, — and her violent language and arrogant bearing had displeased many even of her friends; while others applauded her courage. Of course, exaggerated accounts of her behavior quickly circulated among those who were looking for every pretext to destroy at least her position, if not herself and the institution over which she ruled. She must have raised many enemies against herself during the years of her absolute and domineering rule on Mount Benedict.

There was no school during that Monday morning after my return; confusion and excitement reigned during the hours usually devoted to strict silence. For nine hours daily silence was enforced among the pupils, while I was among them; beside observing it during school-hours, we were obliged to do so at meals, at matin and vesper hours, and in the school-room, except when half-hours of recreation were allowed by the presiding teacher. It seemed to me that I should never become accustomed to those nine daily hours of silence, but the old pupils consoled themselves under their monotony by looking forward to the fête-days, the holidays, and half-holidays, which were frequent during term-time. And a deal of whispering was done by the experienced scholars, who seemed to enjoy forbidden "communication" as it was called, carried on under fear of discovery, better than if it had been permitted.

I could not help noticing how much the poor Sisters were excited on that Monday morning by the condition of things, and how, after all, they seemed to enjoy it. Sister Mary Austin forgot to yawn, and actually laughed aloud as the pupils caricatured the embarrassment of the Selectmen on their Saturday visit, and their awkward manner of filing in and out of the doors. Sounds of similar mirth came through the open windows from the other school-rooms, — it was like an unexpected holiday. Even unwholesome excitements are welcome to people living in such absolute, dull seclusion as did the Nuns, and in their ignorance and innocence they could not foresee the possibility of real danger, when they had done absolutely nothing to deserve it. As for the Superior, her strong will, violent temper, and natural courage made her not unwilling to dwell on the idea of danger which she felt herself strong enough to meet, and she consoled the more timid of the Sisters by telling them that there were Catholic Irishmen enough in Boston to defend them, in case they were attacked.

·On Monday afternoon Mrs. Barrymore the dancing-mistress appeared as usual, full of sympathy with the

Sisters, and indignation at the abominable stories in circulation against the Convent, some of which had got into the papers, besides the oft-repeated legend of the escaped Nun. There was much controversy between the friends and enemies of the Convent as to the truth of these stories, so Mrs. Barrymore said; also as to whether the Boston truckmen would dare to carry out their threats of attacking the building, and whether such violence would or would not be excusable under the circumstances. Mrs. Barrymore, herself a Catholic, laughed at the idea of a mob, and comforted the Nuns with strong expressions of her disbelief. In her excitement she taught the pupils that afternoon *con amore,* and the pupils, equally excited, never " took their steps " more vigorously. Never were higher jumps taken in the *assemblées,* longer runs in the *chassés,* wider circles in the *Pas de Basque.* The lay Sisters whose business it was to dress us sent us all to the dancing-hall in our very best clothes; I suppose it was *their* way of expressing excitement. The Superior came in to look upon us, as was her habit on great occasions when new dances had been learned, or when a favorite pupil was to perform the Highland Fling or the *cachucha* before her admiring schoolmates. We stopped dancing, and turned towards her, courtesying, as she moved among us with gracious dignity, and seated herself at the head of the room. A waltz-quadrille followed, in which

I acquitted myself so well that Mrs. Barrymore patted me on the shoulder with her usual phrase of commendation, " Excellent well, my dear." But yet another honor was in store for me. While I was still blushing with pleasure at this word of praise from the strict Mrs. Barrymore, a little Junior ran up breathless to tell me that I had been selected to *fan the Superior* that afternoon, and to bring me into the Presence.

Behold me, then, mounted on the high stool of honor at the Superior's side, very warm myself after dancing, but afraid to direct the fan in such a way as to take from her any air for the cooling of my own face. I don't know why she chose to give me the privilege of fanning her ; I could not have been a favorite in so short a time, dull and unhappy as I had been from homesickness too. Perhaps she thought it could not outlast this mark of attention, even if my visit to her room on a previous Sunday had failed to cure me. Perhaps she wished to make friends with the Mammon of Unrighteousness at this period of her life, and thought my father's influence might stand her in good stead if she could win his support by graciousness to me. But dear me ! — it just occurs to me, — how strange to find myself accounting so gravely and at such length for so trivial a circumstance ! It shows the strength of that conventual influence which managed to impress even upon the newest pupils the

vital importance of the Superior's every act ; so that
to this day I find myself acknowledging it.

Well, after all, I found my place at the Superior's
side on that Monday afternoon a very interesting one,
especially as she often forgot me and my fan altogether so that I had many opportunities of resting my
arm or fanning myself furtively.   In the intervals of
dancing she would send for certain of the older pupils
— she never beckoned to any one — to come near
her, and she held with them animated conversations
in regard to the circumstances in which she and the
Convent were placed.   She ridiculed unsparingly not
only those who believed the reports against her, but
those who dared to tell her that she was in danger ;
particularly the Selectmen of Charlestown, and their
deputation, whom she called vulgarians, plebeians,
shop-keepers, and what not.   She gloried in her
haughty reception of them, and in her refusal to meet
their wishes ; and the girls, flattered by her condescen-
sion in talking to them as equals, naturally sympathized
and agreed with her, and those who were able out-
did her in sarcasm and vehemence.   Mrs. Barrymore,
too, came up occasionally, wiping her warm face, and
added her word of approval to the indignation-meet-
ing round the Superior's chair.

In the midst of this talk the portress was seen
approaching, passing through the girls with bowed
head and clasped hands, and at last, bending low be-

fore the Superior, " Another Selectman from Charlestown was in the parlor," she said, in the subdued
voice used by the servants in addressing their Sovereign Lady, " and requested to see the Superior on
urgent business." The " Mother Abbess," to use
another of her titles, flamed up at once, and after
scolding the portress roundly, — " For you know I
ordered you not to admit another messenger from
Charlestown on any account," she said, — she ordered
her to go back and shut the door in the man's face, if
nothing else would make him go. The portress made
no answer of course, for the Superior never allowed
such an act of independence, but it was evident she
retired reluctantly to fulfil this command. Soon she
reappeared, still moving humbly forward, but too
much agitated to preserve her usual air of submission.
" Madame, the man refuses to go, and pray hear me,
Madame ! " she supplicated, seeing the Superior about
to burst into a rage ; " he says this Convent is really
in great danger, that even this very night it may be
attacked, — he says the Selectmen have sent him to
get your permission to go into the cellars and examine them thoroughly, so that an affidavit can be
made for the evening papers, — there is nothing
wrong there, Madame, and the Selectmen want to
swear positively that they know it, that they have
seen for themselves, — the man says it may be too
late, even now, but unless such a card is published

this evening they won't answer for the consequences, and it is all they can do for us." I don't remember the exact words, but this is the substance of what the poor frightened portress managed to say, in spite of several violent interruptions from the Superior. Even then that infatuated woman was obdurate. "Stop whimpering, you fool!" she cried, in her imperious way, — "I won't allow my premises to be searched. I'm not afraid of anybody, — the Bishop is my adviser when I need one. The Selectmen of Charlestown are old women, — no doubt they 're afraid. It is their business to protect us, whatever happens, and without any conditions, and send the man back to tell them so."

And now Sister Mary John, tall, thin, angular, entered the room, and hurried up to the Superior, more quickly than etiquette warranted. She was weeping, though she made a great effort to command her tears and to control her trembling voice, so that she might speak with proper submission of manner. She implored the Superior not to send away this man, who came in a friendly spirit; something she added about the value even of one friend in the midst of a community of enemies, and begged to be allowed to accompany the visitor to the cellar of the building, and to show him, herself, every part of the basements that he desired to see. I remember the violent opposition of the Superior to this request, and a vehement,

hurried argument between her and Sister Mary John;
but the latter at length prevailed; indeed, she was in
so very nervous a condition that it was hardly prudent to refuse her.   She hurried away in an eager,
flurried manner, her eyes swollen with crying, her
nose red, — and a large nose is the only feature of her
face I distinctly remember, — and wringing her pocket-
handkerchief between her hands.   Then came a scene
of confusion : the Superior suddenly rose and followed
the Mother Assistant; the school, disturbed by the
unusual interruption, broke up in a hurry; some of
the Sisters appeared among us, greatly excited; some
of the pupils ran into the main hall, others crowded
out upon a balcony overlooking the usual door of
entrance.   A degree of order was at last restored,
and we all flocked into our usual school-rooms.   Here
a hubbub of voices rose, the girls describing to Sister
Mary Austin, and commenting to one another on
what had just passed.   It seems that the Superior,
after leaving the dancing-hall so suddenly, overtook
Sister Mary John on her way to the main cellar door,
lantern in hand, and accompanied by the Selectman,
and, revoking the permission she had given, she positively forbade her to go a step farther.   She snatched
the lantern from the Mother Assistant, thrust it into
the hand of her unlucky companion, flung open the
cellar door, and pointed down the stairs with a per-
emptory gesture.   " There, sir," she cried, " if you

want to play the spy in *my* house, you shall do it
alone. I won't allow any one of the Sisters to enter
that cellar on your account. Go down, sir, with your
lantern, and look about at your leisure, — there is no
man here to prevent you." The poor citizen from
Charlestown hesitated, stepped forward, the gulf below yawned dark as Erebus, he stepped back again;
and at last, fairly daunted by the Superior's eye, he
suddenly put down the lantern, and hurried out of
the building as fast as he could. The Superior's
laugh of derision followed him, and it was echoed by
the girls, who had crowded into the hall to witness
the proceedings. Probably the poor man drew a
breath of relief as he prepared to walk down the
avenue, after leaving the Convent; he was seen to
stop and mop his face, as he emerged from the door,
with a yellow bandanna handkerchief, — another object of ridicule for the girls. But his troubles were
not yet over; he was assailed with a volley of sarcastic
remarks by the pupils, who had rushed out upon the
balcony to watch his departure. Allowed, for the first
time in their experience at the Convent, perfect freedom of speech and of action, they felt bound to take
the part of the Sisters who thus indulged them, and
they were indeed encouraged by those poor unrea-
soning women — big children themselves — to give
their tongues full liberty. " He's afraid, he's afraid,
— he *dares n't*, he *dares n't*," cried some. " He's

tumbled into the ash-heap ; see how pale he is ! " " He was n't afraid, he *did* go down, and he saw a ghost, and that makes him pale," screamed others. " See his pocket-handkerchief, it 's turned yellow with fright," cried a shrill voice. One pupil of a literary turn fired *this* parting shot after the victim of these exquisite witticisms : —

> " Curiosity came from Heaven:
> Its power selectmen knew ! "

" Who wrote *that ?* " asked an admiring friend of this literary young lady afterwards, in the school-room. " Why, don't you know," replied the other with an air, " the man that wrote the First Class Book, of course. I got it out of that." Poor Sister Mary Austin was bewildered with delight and sur-prise, as the girls buzzed about her, telling her how they had tormented and put down " that horrid man " with these impertinences ; she wondered at the ready wit of her pupils.

How well I remember all that happened on that Monday ! As I had not taken any part in the martyr-dom of the unfortunate Selectman, and had cudgelled my brains in vain to get up some remark that should be thought worth listening to in the general fire of wit, I remained unnoticed in the crowd of tall, eager girls, and went about from group to group, attentive to every word that was uttered. The report that the Convent was to be attacked that very night by a mob had spread through the whole school, causing a vast excitement, but no real belief. "Of course," one girl would say, "my papa, who lives in Boston, must know all about it, and he would never let me stay here if such a dreadful thing was going to happen." "Neither would my aunt Jane," "Nor my grandmother either," "Nor uncle Ned," cried one and another, and this seemed to be the opinion of all the girls old enough to reason. "How nice it would be," exclaimed one of the younger girls, "if all our folks in Boston would club together and charter the Charlestown stage, and send for a lot of us to go home tonight!" One of her schoolmates, Katie L——, laughed derisively. "My mamma would send her own private carriage if she thought there was any danger," said Katie, who was a bit of a snob. "Well, what is there odd in my thinking of the Charlestown stage," said the first speaker, "when we have been hearing the noise of carriage-wheels outside, ever since 'dancing' was over? Just as it was on Coronation Day, when the stage was coming and going till dark!" "That's true," remarked another. "I never knew the Superior to have so much company as she has had this afternoon." "I do wish we could see the carriages as well as hear them," said Katie L——. "I dare say my mamma has been here in her carriage this very day, for she and the Superior are great friends, you know."

While she was speaking I noticed the lovely Creole,

Louisa M——, lolling indolently against a desk, on the top of which Susanne P—— was perched cross-legged, her hands clasped round her knees as usual. They were both listening and saying nothing, these girls from the extreme north and south, whose friends were too far away to come to their aid, were it necessary. I remember, because it was a deviation from the customary uniform, that Louise was dressed in a buff crape, made low in the neck, with a surplice waist, as was the fashion then, in which she looked charmingly, and a heavy gold chain, with a cross attached, was clasped round her slender throat. This she was lazily fingering as she reclined, and I noticed the purple discoloration of her almond-shaped nails as she did so. "If my mamma *should* send for me in the carriage," continued Katie L——, who was of a generous nature, "I would make room for you two girls," and she nodded to Louise and Susanne, " because all your folks are so far off, and we 've got any quantity of spare room in our house where you could sleep ; would n't that be nice ? " she added, rather anxiously, as neither of the girls spoke. Louise did not take the trouble to lift her eyelids, heavy with their black lashes, but she opened her red lips just wide enough to murmur, in her slow Spanish accent, "It would be mooch trouble, thank you, — but I hope noting will happen." But Susanne's eyes opened wide, and the light of battle was in them, — how they glowed !

In a loud, clear voice she first said, "But I would not leave !" and then subsided into her usual silence.

Here the Superior entered with even more than her usual *breeziness*, hot and excited, but I never saw her appear tired. She had just dismissed the numerous visitors, some of them parents of pupils, who had driven out of Boston late on that warm afternoon to assure her, and reassure themselves, that there was no danger to be apprehended that night, or any other, from the attack of a mob. Such a thing as a mob did not exist, and never *had* existed in Boston, nor was there material out of which to make one, — such was their unanimous conclusion. We hastily prepared to make obeisance to the Superior on this her unusual appearance among us, but she showed no disposition to exact our reverences, falling into easy talk with those about her, as if she really felt the need of our sympathy. In a few minutes she withdrew as abruptly as she had entered, as if too nervous to remain long quiet in any place.

I observed a small group of the very oldest girls standing together at the end of the room, who had been quiet, moderate, and self-contained all through that day of uproar and confusion. I hastened to join them, half fearing they would repulse me, as they seemed to be talking together with a confidential air. But they did not; indeed, one of the gravest of the girls made way for me to stand at her side, and even allowed me to take her hand, looking down upon me with a kind smile. I could not quite catch the meaning of all that was said, but I perceived that these girls disapproved of all that had been said and done in the Convent that day. They thought the Superior had acted very strangely with regard to the Charlestown Selectmen, particularly on that afternoon. They said she should have allowed Sister Mary John to have accompanied their deputy in his examination of the cellars and basements, — treating him politely, as he only came in the interests of the Convent, and explaining again to him clearly the circumstances relating to the illness of the Mother Assistant. They also thought that the Superior should have condescended to explain to him her relations with the foolish lying girl who had written " Six Months in a Convent," in such a manner as to insure the facts being laid before the public. And they were all disgusted with the behavior of the pupils, who had been so impertinent after the dancing-lesson, and astonished that the Sisters should have been so foolish and thoughtless as to allow and encourage it. But I discovered that they too disbelieved in the coming mob, for, as one of them observed, her father would surely know if anything of the kind was to be apprehended, and he would have sent for her to come home at once, if it was so. Indeed, the pupils, with but few exceptions, big and little, wise and foolish, though they liked the excitement of talking about it, had no real apprehension of danger, feeling sure that their parents and guardians would never leave them to meet it unprotected.

Then I drifted away from these sober-talking Seniors, and encountered Mary H——, of whom I had seen little since her exhortation to me on the first day of my arrival at school. I had observed, however, that she was "naughty" no longer, but, on the contrary, that she held a high place in her class for "deportment" as well as "study," though she was one of the youngest of its members. As we were again schoolmates, it seemed natural that we should continue to be rivals, and in that case that I too, like Miss Edgeworth's Jessie, should *set up for goodness.* I had already suffered considerably in trying to do this at home, for as the oldest of a large family I had been expected to "set a good example" ever since the sister next me in age was a baby in long-clothes. But even if it should turn out that Mary H——'s standard of goodness was too high for me to reach, I was determined to quarrel with her no more, — no, no, we were too old to "get mad," or "put out," with each other, and too old also to "stump" each other to "cut up shines," as Dolly the cook, whom we respectfully addressed as "black lady," used to say. Quarrelling would be improper at our age, and I resolved that we would disagree genteelly, if I found I could not keep my amiable resolution.

So I addressed Mary cordially, and we fell to talking on the great topic of the day ; *would* the Convent be attacked by a mob, and, if so, would the attack be made on that very night ?   Mary and I brought our wits to bear on the question, and as I was really anxious to believe in the coming of the mob, as a way of escape from the Convent, and as Mary was polite and sympathetic, we soon talked each other into a firm faith that something certainly was going to happen, and most likely that very night.   And if so, what was the best way to meet it ?   What could we do to prepare for the mob, in case it *should* come ?   I suggested going to bed in our clothes ; Mary thought that would not be very comfortable, and, besides, Sister Mary Austin would be sure to find us out.   I insisted — at least, if we went to bed dressed, we should be all ready to go home in case the delightful chance *did* arrive.   Mary suggested a compromise, — we would take off our frocks, and slip our nightgowns on over our petticoats, so that we should seem to be all right if Sister Mary Austin chanced to look at us.   I agreed to this, and we promised each other solemnly to carry this plan into effect.   We shook hands upon it.   I was in high spirits, feeling somewhat in this way : as I could not go home unless I *was* dressed, it ought to follow that if I *was* dressed I *should* go home.

" Darling Bella " now called Mary away, and I,

left alone, began to *Pas le Basque* down the school-room, in great sweeps from side to side. But my heart reproached me for its own lightness when I suddenly heard the sound of sobbing, and presently noticed that the cover of one of the desks was raised, and that the sobs came from behind it. It was under shelter of the lids of our desks that we did our cry-ing at school, and it was not considered etiquette to notice any one whose head was hidden in that way. But I ventured to approach this time, and offer con-solation in school-girl fashion, — by putting my arm round the shoulders, shaken with sobs, laying my cheek as close to the cheek of the afflicted one as her pocket-handkerchief would allow, and murmuring words of comfort. To be sure she was a stranger to me, but I felt quite hurt when she suddenly turned her back upon me, jerked me away with her sharp elbow, and muttered, " *Do* let me alone, you ! " I looked at her " particular friend," who sat near, with a dejected countenance. " She's crying because she's afraid that mob's going to come," said the friend, with a solemn shake of the little head. " Is it possible," I thought to myself, " that she is crying for that ? " I am afraid *I* should have wept bitterly if I had been made to believe that the mob was *not* " going to come."

Here a strange voice, calling us to order, made us all start, and the sobbing to cease suddenly. The

Vesper hour had arrived, and poor Sister Mary Austin, feeling herself entirely incapable of reducing us to silence, after she had allowed us to remain so long in such a state of misrule, was obliged to send for Sister Mary Benedict to enforce her authority; the beautiful, strong-minded sister, whose very look compelled obedience, even before her voice commanded it.

We hastened to settle ourselves in our seats, under her cold, severe eye, and when order was entirely restored and silence reigned, a monitor was chosen to watch over the school-room, and, though they knew it not, the Nuns departed to join with their companions in the last Vesper service they should ever hold in that house. The remembrance of that hour, even now, fills me with solemnity. No one thought of rebelling against long-accustomed authority, now that Sister Mary Benedict had made us feel that our period of license was over, and the girls subsided quickly into a stillness so deep that I thought I could hear the beating of their hearts, as well as the hurried breathing, which could not be controlled at once after so long a period of strong excitement. Yet when the solemn Vesper-music stole upon the silence, rising and falling in minor cadences, the reaction came, the excitement gradually abated, and I am sure those of the girls who could *feel* the meaning of that plaintive singing must have shared the vague yet real apprehension and anxiety that gave such wondrous expression to the voices of those poor Sisters.

At any rate, we all went up to bed in serious mood, just as the twilight was fading, — for I don't think I have mentioned the early hour of retirement at the Convent, half-past seven for Seniors and Juniors alike,—and at the time of year of which I write there was just light enough at that hour for us to undress without the lantern, which, in winter, swung from the ceiling of the room, and just made darkness visible.

My cot was next but one to an end window, and the young girl who occupied the bed between me and that window had not made her appearance at school since the close of vacation, so that for the time I enjoyed the privilege of a double-bedded room, and by just turning my head to the right, a wide sky view through the uncurtained panes that belonged to the corner of my privileged neighbor. The oldest Williams sister slept next the end window opposite, but I did not feel enough acquainted with her to hazard any whispered remark across the "middle passage," though I was very anxious to know what her opinion really was as to the probable events of the night. I suspect she thought very little about the matter, for she undressed quickly with many loud and long yawns, and was in bed and asleep before I had managed to slip off my frock and put on my night-

gown over the rest of my clothing, for I was resolved
to keep my agreement with Mary, and to go to bed
dressed, if Sister Mary Austin's argus eyes would let
me, — she usually kept so close a watch on our toilet
proceedings. That night, however, she went through
her duties mechanically, and took very little notice of
us, so that I had the happiness of carrying out my
plan, and of lying in my petticoats, in a delightful
perspiration, with the bedclothes closely drawn up
under my chin, so as to hide any peculiarity in my
appearance, should the Sister glance at me in her
nightly promenade down the " middle aisle " of the
dormitory. Mary's bed was near the door, a long
way from mine, and though I strained my eyes in the
fading twilight, trying to watch her, I could not see
whether or no she had kept her part of our agreement
not to undress that night.

And now Sister Mary Austin had made her final
passage through the dormitory, murmuring her prayers
with abstracted look, had paused at the door to cross
herself, and utter her final " Benedicite," or whatever
pious Latin phrase serves a Religieuse for a formal
" good night," and had shut us in to repose. As for
me, I was so wide awake that I could not even close
my eyes, and I lay, I knew not how long, but it
seemed to me for half the night, listening to the deep
breathing, mingled with an occasional snore, of my
room-mates, who were quite weary enough to fall

asleep at once. A few uneasy ones stirred on their pillows and muttered some unintelligible words, perhaps still disturbed by the excitement of the day, for the most dyspeptic would not have been made restless by our supper of dry bread and milk.

In the midst of these heavy sleepers I felt myself alone in the room, and, becoming more and more uncomfortable and hot under my petticoats, I determined to stay in bed no longer. So I rose softly and ventured to steal to the end window, in the alley of my absent neighbor, from which a glimpse of the avenue and the Bishop's house was visible. I even had the courage to raise the window, very gently, and the summer night-wind suddenly blowing in my face made me feel as if I had actually stepped out doors. I folded my arms on the window-sill, and leaned out as far as I could, that I might give myself up to the illusion of fancying myself out in the night alone, when all the world but me was asleep.

The Convent, on the summit of Mount Benedict, stood so high that I seemed to be lifted up among the stars that sparkled and twinkled like heavy golden drops around and above me. The breeze, steadily blowing, stirred me to vague imaginings of distant beauty and sweetness, for it was laden with perfume from the wooded hills a long way off. For the Convent stood between the sea and an amphitheatre of hills, whose slopes were covered with villages, villas,

and gardens, and the charming suburbs of a great
city, while their summits were still crowned with
rich groves of trees.   But just outside the Convent
grounds, and around the base of Mount Benedict,
lay, like an encircling ring, that barren, clayey district,
given up to brickmaking, from out of which the city
of Boston was springing.   This region of clay-pit appeared so ugly, dull, and desolate, when we looked
down upon it from our bowery playground on Mount
Benedict during recreation hours, that I never will-
ingly suffered my eyes to dwell upon it, overlooking it
quickly to let them rest instead upon the green and
purple distance.   But on this night such a change appeared as made a fairy land of that distant plain.   All
the brick-kilns had been set burning, and as night concealed the ugly brickyards and clay-fields in which they
were erected, nothing was visible but the magic circle
of fire that seemed to be drawn around the Convent.

No sound was to be heard but the crackling of the
kiln-fires, the far-away bark of a dog, the monotonous
droning of the late grasshoppers, and the vague hum
and stir of insects and leaves on a summer night.
These, then, are the " Voices of the Night," I mused,
calling to mind a book with that title which had been
given to my mother.

The breeze was so cooling, so refreshing, the distant
sounds so soothing, that insensibly I grew sleepy and
my head drooped lower and lower, till my cheek

touched my folded arms. I made an effort to waken myself and to hold up my heavy head, and opened my eyes to their full width, for which I was rewarded by seeing a bright falling star curve down to the horizon.

For one instant I watched it; the next was the first moment in my life when I realized the meaning of the word *appalled.* I heard — what shall I call it ? — a shout, a cry, a howl, a yell ? It was the sound of a mob, a voice of the night, indeed, that made it hideous. Child as I was, I knew at once the meaning of the sound, — it came from more than a mile away, for, as we heard afterwards, the mob gave one roar as it crossed Charlestown bridge, and then observed profound silence till it reached the Convent grounds. My heart beat thick and fast, my hands clasped themselves together, and there was a rushing and ringing in my ears, as if the mob was surging around me already. But in a few moments I recovered myself, and drew back into the dormitory from the window. The girls still slept profoundly, and not a sound was audible about the building ; that distant cry, so significant to me, was not loud enough to awaken any sleeper.

Once more I ventured to put my head out of the window, and waited for what would come next, in a trance of suspense, hardly daring to breathe. Again the watch-dog barked, at the far-away farm-house, the grasshoppers droned, the fires in the brickyards crackled, but how changed was the night to my excited imagination! Save for those faint noises, solemn silence again reigned, but I knew it was to be broken, horribly broken, and I shivered all over in the anticipation. I looked up at the stars, vaguely fancying that the worlds above would in some way be changing, in sympathy with the world below, and half surprised to see them still in their places, throbbing with the same measured beat.

Though I leaned, waiting, against the window, still as a little statue, my brain was whirling with thought. Yes, the mob was really coming, — Mary and I were right. I, for one, was dressed, and could in a moment slip on my frock, if necessary, but what would happen? At least I should have to go home, — the mob would do something to make *that* necessary. Very likely there would be an end to the school, at least for a time. Delightful thought! Courage came back to me at the bare idea. Welcome the mob if it could bring that about! " Destruction of the Convent," — yes, the girls had repeated that phrase many times, — when? Yesterday? To-day? Why, it seemed an age since I heard them talking about it, and how still it was, how silent! The dog had done barking, — he must have gone to sleep, and no wonder, for I had been waiting an eternity. Did I really, after all, hear that cry? Perhaps I dreamed it ; that would be natural enough when my head was full of mobs, and the girls had talked of nothing else — to-day? yesterday? which was it? Ah! — A horrible yell suddenly rent the air within a few yards of the window at which I was standing, and a host of dark figures rushed into view, turning the corner of the Bishop's house, rolling over the ground, as it seemed in the dim starlight, like a black cloud. I flew across the room to Elizabeth Williams's bed, shaking her and crying out, " Wake up, wake up, the mob has really come ! " She started up scream- ing ; indeed, though the rioters had gone round to the front of the house, and were no longer visible from our windows, which looked another way, the hoarse outcry they made would have roused the Seven Sleepers.

All the girls in the dormitory suddenly wakened, screamed in concert with Elizabeth, and many of them sprang out of bed in affright. I could just discern their figures moving helplessly about in the darkness. Suddenly the door opened, and Sister Mary Austin appeared ; by the light of a lantern swinging from the hall ceiling opposite the door I could see that she was shaking all over, but she tried to control the trembling of her voice, as she called out, " Girls, don't be frightened ! There can't be any danger, but you had better dress yourselves." The younger girls ran up to her, and clung to her

6

screaming, " O, the mob, the mob, — we shall all be
killed !   O, what *shall* we do, what *will* become of
us ? "   The older ones wept and wailed and wrung
their hands, and those who were intimate friends
threw their arms about each other, and vowed to keep
together whatever happened.   Sister Mary Austin,
herself weeping hysterically, kept imploring the girls
to dress themselves, whenever she could command
her voice, and the poor things essayed to do so, but
they were so agitated, so bewildered, that few of them
were able to put on all their clothes, or to fasten
properly such as they *did* contrive to get into.   It
was not for want of time, for we had hours yet to
wait before the will of the mob declared itself ; perhaps the want of light had something to do with the
strange helplessness of the scholars, — of course no
lamp was allowed in any room with windows, lest the
mob should be attracted by it, — and the dim glimmer
of the hall lantern only puzzled the poor children
whose eyes were blinded with tears and terror.   As
for me, I managed to take off my nightgown and put
on my frock, and then I sat quietly down on my
trunk, feeling a sort of contempt for the insane terror
of all the people about me, kept at its climax by the
furious outcries of the rioters.   Indeed, I should give
myself credit for feeling the high courage of a heroine,
if I had not to confess that my common-sense whispered to me, from the first, that the girls had nothing

to fear from the hands of the mob, who probably considered them as objects of pity. It was the Superior
whom they specially hated, and her Nuns and her
Convent, and on these was to be spent the wrath
and rage born of religious bigotry. This thought
made me calm and fearless, though it was rather an
instinct than a thought, for of course it did not present itself definitely to my mind. So I sat on my
trunk and listened to the cries of the rioters, and the
responsive wailing of the girls, oddly mingled with
fretful complainings, like children as they were, —
" O dear, I can't find the bottom of my petticoat ! "
" O mercy, this shoe is n't mine, I can't make it go
on at heel ! "   " O, my frock, the sleeve is wrong side
out, or something ; it won't go on ! "   " Where *is*
my other stocking ?   It 's away under your bed, Jane,
I never *can* get it ! "   " What shall I ever do ?   My
flannel petticoat has got wet all over in my wash-
bowl ! "

And now we heard two gunshots fired in rapid
succession outside the Convent, and simultaneously
loud screams issued from every dormitory where the
scholars were collected. Some one rushed into our
dormitory, crying out, " They have shot the Superior ;
she went to the top of the high steps to speak with
them, and they would n't listen, and they shot her."
Poor Sister Mary Austin sank back on her chair in
strong hysterics at this word, and a scene of great

confusion ensued; some of the older girls tried to
help the poor Sister as well as their trembling limbs
would let them; they fanned her and dashed water
in her face. Another messenger entered and shook
Sister Mary Austin by the shoulder. "Do you hear
me?" she said, — it was some tall girl from a neighboring dormitory, whom I did not know by name, —
" the Superior is not hurt; they shot at her, but they
did not hit her. O Sister! do stop crying so terribly,
do hear me, — the Superior is just as safe as you
are, and she 'll be here very soon, and you can see her
for yourself."

Poor Sister Mary Austin sat up, gasping for breath,
and although I had not recovered from the terrible
impression made upon me by those gunshots, I was
struck with the ridiculous appearance of the poor lady,
with her veil drenched, her linen head-piece half off,
disclosing her round shaven poll. Ludicrous ideas
always seize most strongly upon me in the midst of
horror.

Now we heard a quick, firm step coming through
the hall, attended by a patter of little feet; and in a
moment the Superior herself was among us, sur-
rounded by a crowd of Juniors, trembling little things
who had forgotten their awe of her and clung to her
desperately. Many of us ran to meet her at the door,
and I among the number, eager to know what had
really befallen her. Sister Mary Austin clutched her

dress with nervous eagerness, and the Superior looked
down upon her with her usual grand air, though she
was evidently excited to the highest pitch. It was
difficult to catch what she said through the chorus of
fear and lamentation which the children about her
kept up, but her eyes flashed, as I could see by the
rays from the lantern which happened to fall upon
her as she stood near the door. It seems that the
mob had never ceased to call upon her name, from the
moment they reached the front of the building, order-
ing her, with oaths and savage outcries, to come forth,
and bring with her the miserable victims whom she
kept imprisoned in her dungeons. The Superior
would have gone out and confronted the rioters immediately had she not been restrained by the Nuns,
who clung to her with prayers and tears, and entreated
her not to venture into unnecessary danger. For a
long time they held her back, but she had the courage
of a man, and the taunts and jeers of the mob stung
her to recklesesnss, and she at last tore herself from
the arms of the Sisters, and rushed out upon the
landing of the high flight of steps that gave access
to the main door of the building. Though she had
the courage of a man, she was as ignorant of the
world as a child, and utterly wanting in tact. She
had been used to command all her life, and she
looked upon the mob with unmeasurable contempt,
— as *canaille*, as creatures that could be cowed by

threats. I can imagine how she appeared as she stood on the top of the steps high above them, her tall erect figure dimly outlined in the starlight, her black robes fluttering back and blending with the dark background which the open door made behind her. The mob saluted her with a storm of objurgation, which she bore without flinching, interrupting them at last in her clear, loud voice, with some word that intimated her desire to speak. Curiosity as to what she would say caused a sudden silence to fall on the rioters, and it is possible that if she had known how to address them she might have prevailed with them and persuaded them to disperse. For they seemed at first by no means determined to commit violence, in spite of their savage threats to that effect. It can hardly be believed possible, but such was the fact, that the Superior addressed that listening crowd in language as violent as their own, delivered with the utmost arrogance and imperiousness of manner. I never knew what her words really were, with the exception of one threat, which I myself heard her boast of having made; and if she uttered it to the mob with half the angry vehemence that she used in repeating it afterwards, I do not wonder that she excited violent indignation. " Disperse immediately," she said to the rioters ; " for if you don't, the Bishop has twenty thousand Irishmen at his command in Boston, and they will whip you all into the sea ! "

Think of the effect of such a speech as that on a body
of American truckmen and mechanics! It was immediately after she had launched this threat at the
rioters that, breaking their silence with fierce yells,
they fired at the Superior twice, and the affrighted
Nuns, hovering in the shadow of the door behind her,
pulled her back by force, and barred the door in the
face of the mob.

Even then it did not proceed to extremities, — we
had yet a long time to wait! All the dormitories
were at the back of the building, looking upon the
garden, which, as is usual in convents, was entirely
shut in by high fences, and the same strong picket-
fences, built out on each side of the main façade,
cut off all communication between the grounds at the
front and those at the back of the Convent. It was
from the end window of one of the Senior dormitories,
at right angles with the front avenue, that I caught
the first glimpse of the rioters passing through it.

Profound silence and darkness by the Superior's
orders reigned in the lower story of the building, and
in the front up-stairs rooms; but the girls moved
freely through the back dormitories, as these were
farther removed from the sight and sound of the mob,
unless, indeed, it should break down the separating
fences, or force a passage into the house. Tired of
sitting on my trunk, waiting for I knew not what, I
too wandered about in the dormitories, always seeing

a succession of painful sights.   In one the poor
Novice, her pale face laid back into her white veil,
was stretched on a bed in a dead faint, waited upon
by some of the girls, who, however, hardly knew what
to do for her.   In another Rosamond Moriarty lay
on the floor in a fit, her weak nerves being quite unable to bear the terror of the night.   Several of the
children had hysterics more or less severe, and the
sound of their laughing, crying, and groaning was
dismal indeed.   I don't remember encountering individual girls in my wanderings, — probably in my
state of exaltation I met them, and looked at them
without recognizing them.   One only I remember.
The front rooms opposite the dormitories were closed
by the Superior's order, to shut out as much as possible the noise made by the rioters, but as I happened to notice one of these doors ajar, while I was
lingering in the hall, I ventured to push it open.
There, alone, sitting on the sill of an open window,
her face and figure visible in the light thrown up
from some lanterns carried by the men below, sat
Susanne Perrault !   She looked up calmly as I entered, but said nothing ; and made way for me to
come and sit beside her.   Seeing her so composed,
I went up to her, whispering, " O Susanne, how
dare you ! " for it was reported among the girls that
stones had been thrown at the few among them who
had been reckless enough to appear near a front win-

dow. " I have been here a long time," she said
quietly, in her pretty broken English; "no one has
noticed me, — come and look ! "

I ventured to put my head over the window-sill,
and I saw below me a crowd of men and a few
lanterns, moving together confusedly, and I heard a
jargon of voices, though I could not distinguish much
that was said. Some were in eager consultation,
apparently; there was much talk interrupted with
oaths; savage tones struck my ear; foul language
was uttered that I could not understand, and the
Superior's name often mentioned, never without an
oath and some insulting appellation. One sentence
only I clearly remember; for it was spoken right beneath us, and so distinctly uttered that I think it
was said to frighten us, by some one who saw us at
the window. "Sad enough for the poor girls," said
the voice, " but there is no help for it, — we must
blow up this cursed building with gunpowder."

I drew my head in quickly; perhaps I should have
been frightened had I not looked at Susanne, and
taken courage from her contemptuous smile. Some
one else must have overheard this speech, or one like
it, from another window, for on leaving Susanne
alone at her post of observations, I found the poor
girls suffering from a new access of terror, caused by
a report that we were all going to be blown up. A
few years after I was told that Susanne Perrault was

the sister of Louis Perrault, who, with his father, were prominent leaders of the Canadian rebellion, and who took rank as heroes in the minds of Canadian sympathizers. Certainly Susanne, the daughter of the house, was a born heroine !

The mob had now been before the Convent for an hour or *two ;* it seemed a long, long time, though we had no way of measuring it. With the exception of certain gusts of terror which swept through the children when some new, dreadful threat of the rioters, uttered more distinctly than usual, was reported among them, the excitement that completely overwhelmed them at first had subsided, and the poor weary girls had fallen into a state of passive endurance. Many of them seemed stupefied as they sat about on their trunks or on the floor, leaning against the foot of a bedstead, for there was not a single chair in the dormitories. Some were dozing as they lay stretched across the foot of a bed ; some had taken pillows, and had thrown themselves down to rest in the alleys between the cots. There seemed to be a general feeling that it was not the thing at such a time to lie down properly on the bed in the usual manner. And all were in different stages of dress and undress, hardly one fitly attired, for the Nuns were entirely absorbed in their own terrors, and not one paid the least attention to the condition of the pupils, or even at any time suggested to them to try and save such valuable articles as could be easily carried from the wreck and ruin that was to be apprehended.

Suddenly the calm into which we had fallen was broken by a joyful cry : " They are going off ! The mob is really going off ! They have left the Convent, and they are all moving in a body towards Charles-town ! " Even the most timid of the girls hastened to look out of the front windows, anxious to see for themselves if this wonderful, delightful news *could* be true. All was pleasant flutter, and a joyful excitement succeeded to the late melancholy state of suspense, for the mob were indeed moving off, and had already left the front of the building. We could see the black cloud of figures rolling along the terrace-walks leading to the main avenue that wound its way down the hill to Charlestown. I rushed to the room where Susanne Perrault still sat motionless on the window-sill, and followed the cloud with my eyes as it slowly retreated.

I heard the laughing and chattering of the girls, so suddenly relieved from apprehension, in the neighboring rooms, but I could not say one word. I confess to a horrible feeling of disappointment. I had so hoped that the mob might do *something* that would lead to my going home and to the breaking up of the school, though very vague in my mind was the idea of what that *something* might, could, or should be.

Susanne was equally silent, and paid no attention to me whatever. At last I could contain myself no longer, and I said, mournfully, " So they are really going away, after all ! " And I heaved a deep sigh. "You are mistaken," said Susanne, quietly. " Tu te trompes," she muttered, forgetting her English in the earnestness with which she watched the proceedings of the mob. " Look there ! " she exclaimed aloud, and I looked with all my eyes.

At the end of the terrace-walks, and before descending the hill, the black cloud wavered and stopped ; then it rolled back and forth in various uncertain directions, then it settled, and, after what seemed a long time, the light from a couple of bonfires began to illumine the scene. These were fed with boards and pickets from the fences at the bottom of the walks ; we could see men pulling and tearing them away, and throwing them upon the bonfires, which then emitted great showers of sparks. I thought the light was already growing very brilliant, when suddenly the flames from some burning tar-barrels blazed out fiercely, streaming high up in the air, putting out the light of the fainter bonfires and making the place as light as day. The black cloud resolved itself entirely into the figures of men, which moved irregularly about the fires.

Soon we heard a faint tinkling sound, and we saw a speck of dim light like that of a lantern hung high on a frail support, come moving and creeping up the hill from the main road to Charlestown. "Susanne, what is it?" I whispered. "It is the fire-engine from Charlestown," she answered. "They have seen the blaze; they thought it must be from the Convent, that it was on fire, and they have come to put it out." "Then they will certainly help us, those firemen," I whispered again, for I was too much excited to speak loud. "They certainly will drive the mob off," I went on, hardly knowing whether I wished they would or not! There was a pause when the engine reached the top of the hill, apparently a parley between the rioters and the firemen. "Now look again," said Susanne, in her quiet tone; the lantern, swinging high above the engine, turned round slowly, drew off from the rioters, began to descend the hill. Down, down, down it went, swaying from side to side, while the engine-bell tinkled, tinkled ever more faintly, and slowly the machine disappeared from our straining eyes, and was lost from sight ere it turned sharp round into the road.

The little opposition made to their doings by the firemen seemed to give the rioters sudden courage, which, as we afterwards heard, was stimulated also by liquor,— a barrel of spirit, probably New England rum, having been broached in the neighborhood of the bonfires, — and an entire change took place in their conduct, hitherto so vacillating. They leaped and danced about the blazing tar-barrels, yelling, singing, throwing their arms about in wild gestures, so that their figures, seen against the brilliant light of the flames, looked like a confusion of black whirling wheels, whose spokes were legs and arms. Suddenly some of the number ran to the bonfires, snatched from them burning firebrands, which they whirled aloft, and, loudly calling on the rest to follow, they placed themselves at the head of the dreadful returning tide of rioters, which now surged back towards the Convent with a hoarse roar like a great wave rising to ingulf it.

Now, indeed, there was no mistaking the purpose of the rioters, their time for action had come; and the poor children, still watching at the front windows, and just now so happy in the relief of their fears, saw it and knew it as well as I did. A great cry arose, and then an agonized and confused screaming from the poor creatures. I remember no more of Susanne than if she had disappeared by magic from before my eyes; I rushed back to the hall, where I encountered a crowd of distracted children, running in every direction. Suddenly I heard voices calling out, " Maria Fay, where is Maria Fay? The Superior wants Maria Fay "; and I caught a glimpse of some of the Nuns urging that lovely young creature into a front room. I did not follow her, but I know that she was there seized upon by the Superior, and put forward as

a forlorn hope by that poor lady and her terrified
group of Nuns, at their wits' ends for means to meet
the coming destruction. I heard a window in that
room thrown open ; and, running back to the post of
observation I had just quitted, I was in time to catch
a glimpse of Maria's head and body thrust out of the
window so far that it was evident she was grasped
from behind by some unseen hand, and to hear her
youthful treble pipe forth, " Go away, go away ! my
father 's a judge, and he will put you all in prison ! "
This address to the mob, of course, produced not the
least effect, probably it was not even heard, but poor
Maria had done her best ; she was hastily jerked back
by the hands that held her, and the window shut
down. The Superior really thought that her idea
of threatening the mob with the terrors of the law,
by the mouth of a judge's daughter, was an inspira-
tion of genius sure to be successful, though such be-
nighted ignorance of life and human nature is almost
impossible to believe !

This solemn farce being concluded, and Maria's
head disappearing, the ever-increasing yells of the
mob, now swarming once more under the walls of
the building, drove me also from the window, and I
ran back again into the hall, where I found the
Superior trying to rally the children, who were wildly
running about here and there. Her strong will prevailed over many, who came clustering about her.

With her quick eye she singled out those of the older girls who seemed to have the most presence of mind. To each of them she intrusted one of the smallest of the children at her knees, with a few solemn words of charge, clasping their hands together with her own firm palm. Suddenly her eye fell on me, and she almost smiled. " Why, you are as brave as a little lion ! " she said, and, drawing me up to her with one hand, she brought forward with the other a small, sickly, thin child, whose pink frock was dropping off her skeleton shoulders. The poor little creature was perfectly dazed with terror and bewilderment, and the Superior looked at her keenly, as she put her helpless hand into mine. " Her mind is gone to-night entirely," said she, " and I give her in charge to you, because you are not frightened. Promise me solemnly that you won't let go her hand, till you find yourself in some safe place." Her voice and manner made a great impression on me; I looked up into her face and gave the required promise, at the same time squeezing the poor little girl's hand so hard that she gave a little moan.

I shall never cease to wonder at the personal coolness and courage of the Superior in this fearful crisis ; as remarkable as the childish ignorance and want of tact she showed in the management of others. For the mob, brutalized with drink, rending the air with hoarse outcries, were already endeavoring to force the

heavy outer doors with violent blows, which re-
sounded through the building, and shook it to its
foundation. And the Superior knew that if these
rioters should come upon her, inflamed with liquor,
rage, and hate as they were then, they would kill her.
Yet her eye never quailed, and neither hand nor
voice trembled.

I don't know how the time went. I suppose it was
only for a minute or two that we stood paralyzed in
the hall, listening to the violent attack being made on
the doors below. Suddenly a black body of Nuns
came flying through the whole length of the passage
from the Superior's room, and threw themselves
upon her, pushing her forward, and crying, " O
Madame, O ma Mère, they have entered your
room, they are climbing in through the window, it is
full of men already, — they will be here in a moment,
— O, fly, fly ! — O, *where* shall we go ? " And they
wept and groaned frantically. " Silence ! " cried the
Superior, in her commanding voice. " Mes Sœurs,
follow me ! and you girls," she added, hastily turning to us, " if any of you are willing to run the
risk of coming with me, do you keep close beside
me." She then ran forward through the hall, followed by the Nuns, and by many of the girls, the big
ones dragging their little charges after them, till she
reached a certain stairway. Here she paused to look
back at her following, and just then a crash was

7

heard below, so sudden and deafening, that the violent screams of women and children above and the triumphant hurrahs of the mob beneath were hardly audible above it.   No wonder the sound was overwhelming !   Well-directed volleys of stones were fired simultaneously and in quick repetition at all the lower front windows of the building, and the crashing of glass was as loud as a volley of musketry. Some of the girls who were following the Superior, not knowing what they did in their terror, ran past her with a wild shriek, farther down the long hall,, and vanished from sight, nor did she attempt to stop them.   She herself flew down the stairs, and I saw that she held a large key in her hand.   Just at the bottom of these stairs a massive door opened from the lower back hall into a small paved court, sunk between two long projecting wings of the main building ; and from this court there was access to the large back garden of the Convent.   All the Nuns, and about twenty of the girls, prepared to follow the Superior, but when they saw her put the large key which she carried into the lock of the court door, with a natural hesitation they lingered at the top of the stairs, not knowing who or what might rush in upon them as soon as that door should be opened. As for me, I was wrought up to a pitch of heroism ; indeed, I don't think that I screamed once during that night, even in sympathy with the screaming multitude around me, and, seeing the Superior all alone at the foot of the stairs essaying to unlock the door, I broke through the trembling crowd on the landing above and hurried down to join her, as fast as I could drag my passive charge after me. " Brave girl ! " she said, as I pressed close to her side ; nor can I describe the feelings which agitated me during the moment of suspense when she was turning the heavy lock of the door. The stillness without made that moment still more exciting ; I imagined a band of crouching rioters in ambush just outside the door, and prepared myself for the sudden spring of a drunken mob, ready to beat down the Superior and the Nuns with clubs, or shoot at them with guns. I think the Superior shared my apprehensions, for she drew a long shuddering breath as she at length mastered the lock, and flung the door wide open. Ah ! shall I ever forget the ghostly stillness of that courtyard ? It struck me with awe, as something supernatural, in contrast with the horrible din of destruction at the front of the building. Shall I ever forget how calmly the moonlight slept upon its fair pavement, save when the small shadows of leaves, stirred by the night-wind, moved lightly over it, like fairy feet dancing ? The court was planted with white-rose bushes, yet in bearing, and shall I ever forget how the full-blown roses were set among the dusky branches, like so many ivory cups, nor how

they seemed to hold a sweeter perfume than ever rose-
cups held before? For, as I stood at the Superior's
side, close enough to feel the beating of her heart
while she was struggling with the unyielding lock, I
had so wrought myself up to expect, and to meet,
nameless horrors in that courtyard, that the reaction
set my imagination free to enjoy and idealize the
peaceful reality.

Well for the Superior it was, that her room contained many valuable articles, besides a large sum of
money just paid in by the pupils; for, if the men who
first climbed into it through her windows had not
stopped to steal her possessions, she could never have
had time to escape from the upper hall as she did.

As soon as the anxious little crowd waiting at the
top of the stairs saw the Superior disappearing in
safety through the court door they all rushed tumul-
tuously after her, and we followed her quickly to the
very bottom of the long garden, where our further
progress was stopped by a board fence, some eight or
ten feet high. As it had been built strong enough to
keep *out* all curious intruders and garden thieves, of
course it effectually shut us *in*. The Superior led
the way to the very door of the solid brick tomb,
which was as large as a small house, and made us
all sit down on the grass-border of the broad walk
leading past it. The iron door of the tomb was ajar,
perhaps for the purpose of ventilation, and I think the

Superior meant to take refuge within it, should she
be followed by the rioters.

And now profound silence was again enjoined upon
us by the Superior, who sat enthroned among us, —
for she always held herself enthroned like a queen,
however lowly her position, — and the Nuns crouched
about her feet. The moon, which had but lately
risen, and which began to be obscured by light
clouds, occasionally revealed the figures of the
girls, who, motionless in various hopeless attitudes,
had withdrawn themselves as much as possible into
the shade of the bushes that lined the garden paths.
Some of them slept the sleep of utter exhaustion,
in spite of the horrible noise. For the mob, after
forcing their way into the Convent, quickly overran it
from garret to cellar, and the work of its destruction
proceeded rapidly. With fascinated eyes I watched
its progress, for I sat where I could see the building
from top to bottom. The rioters began their work by
ransacking the cellars and basements, probably looking for those dungeons and cells of which they had
heard, and which they chose to believe were used by
the Superior as places of punishment for such Nuns
among the Community as fell under her displeasure,
and their voices, underground, sounded like the
hoarse growling of a pent-up sea. Up stairs, at the
same time, a few wandering lights crossed the windows hurriedly, and moved from room to room quickly,

carried probably by certain practical spirits, who
were taking advantage of the opportunity to search
for such valuables as they could pocket easily.   Soon
lights and figures mounted from story to story, and a
moving panorama of rioters crossed and recrossed the
windows in procession.   The noise of breaking and
tearing down heavy furniture, the smashing and crashing of glass, pictures, and china, began to rise above
the din and dissonance of voices ; occasionally some
window would suddenly be cleared of figures, and
with a rush of rioters from within, certain large
pieces of furniture would fill the gap for a moment,
and then thunder down upon the pavement below,
followed by the hurrahs and jeering laughter of the
crowd.   Sundry harps and guitars were destroyed in
this way, and the sharp snap and melancholy after-
wail of their broken strings, as they fell, put into my
mind the sudden thought, " O, what if they *should*
throw out one of the Sisters ! "

And still we sat in profound silence, the girls
effacing themselves as much as possible among the
shrubs, the Nuns huddled together, hiding their faces
in their veils, about the knees of the Superior, who,
erect and motionless, kept her eyes fixed on the
doomed Convent, where she had so long held ar-
bitrary rule.   Whenever the night-wind rustled suddenly in the branches of the trees, or sent the fallen
leaves scurrying along the garden-walks, we fancied

for a moment that the sounds were made. by stealthy footsteps approaching, and our hearts beat fast. I heard the low sigh of relief breathed by such of my companions as were awake, when the cause of the sudden sounds made themselves evident. For when the faint moonlight broke through the clouds, I saw some of the children still asleep, with heads nodding on their breasts. The poor little child put under my care by the Superior, and who could not have been more than six years old, lay across my lap, either asleep or stupefied, and I still held her hand grasped mechanically in mine, in fulfilment of my promise. In answer to a whispered inquiry, she told me that her name was Louisa, that she came from New Orleans. Occasionally during this dreary time of waiting the poor little thing would stir her head uneasily in my lap, and mutter something, as if in a dream, — waking or sleeping, I knew not which, — about " Mother " or "Aunt Fän," or a certain wax-doll whose remembrance seemed to haunt her brain. And I had plenty of time to think of my poor Claribel, and wonder at my folly in not making an attempt to save her. I don't know to this day why I did not, for there was nothing to hinder me from groping my way to the school-room at any time during the hours when the mob were keeping us in suspense till they should have made up their minds what to do with us.

And now the windows of the Convent began to be

illuminated, one after the other, and commencing in
the second story, with a more brilliant light,   No
candles, lamps, or torches, such as the rioters had
been carrying through the rooms, could account for
it.   For they were firing the Convent.   I could see
men going from room to room, heaping all sorts of
combustible materials, bedding, curtains, clothing,
into the middle of the floors, and even flinging
school-books upon the piles, which came down with
fluttering leaves, like big birds swooping upon them.
After an ominous pause I saw the fire burst from
these combustible heaps, at first feebly, and then, as
it were, stretching its arms higher and higher toward
the ceiling, palpitating and brightening as if breathing
in a new life.   As soon as the rioters had made sure
that each fire was well lighted, they rushed from the
room where they had kindled it and went to work
elsewhere, till in a very short time the windows of the
Convent began to glow like openings into a world of
flames.   Again there arose the sounds of destruction ;
of rending, tearing, and falling of heavy weights, and
the shivering and crackling of glass, but made by
a power stronger than the hands of a dozen mobs.
These were the most horrible moments of all that
horrible night, and the noise was aggravated by the
increased roaring of the fire, which, together with the
brilliancy of its light and the pungent smell of smoke,
threw the poor women and children about me into a

stronger agony of terror than ever ; the harder to bear
because it had to be suppressed.   For we all felt that
the time must come soon when we should be discovered.   The rioters, driven from the building by the
fire, would assuredly turn to fresh mischief ; probably
nothing had prevented the Superior from being followed long before but the ignorance of the mob as to
the nature of convents.   They had no idea the poor
Sisters were waiting for them at the bottom of the
garden, but of course supposed they could walk out
of it at pleasure, and probably had done so.   But if
the search for the Superior should commence, the
rioters knew she could not have escaped them at the
front of the Convent, and would follow her through
the garden, sure that she must have taken that way to
a place of refuge.

And the very last of the rioters seemed about quit-
ting the building ; a few lingered yet in the music-
room, and they must have been wild with intoxication
or excitement, for their last act, before leaving the
room, was actually to hoist up and throw from the
window a piano, which fell with a crash distinctly
audible above all other sounds ; then, with one final
yell, the ruffians disappeared from our sight.   Every
moment we were growing more and more anxious and
distracted.   What should we do ? where could we
go ?   We were shut up in that garden as closely as
if we were in prison, with no place even of temporary

refuge from the rioters but the tomb, and the poor girls held the tomb in as much horror as they did the rioters. Through the whole of that eventful night the same fears and apprehensions were shared by all, and though very few words were exchanged, each of us knew sympathetically what the rest were feeling. I suppose I was the only child among them all who was buoyed up under the terrors of the night by the delightful hope of deliverance from the Convent and a return to liberty I am sure the rioters would have exulted over me as *one* victim released by them from the Superior's rule, had they known my state of mind.

I was beginning to feel very much cramped by long sitting on the grass. I had raised up poor Louisa, and was trying to prop her head against my shoulder while I wrapped my frock about her bare neck and arms, when I fancied I heard suspicious sounds, as of people walking softly on the other side of the fence. I held my breath to listen; there could be no mistake this time; no rustling of foliage or fluttering of leaves ever produced such sounds. And there were several footsteps audible together, as if a number of men were creeping along towards us, one after another. We all heard them plainly; for a moment the terrified children sat paralyzed with new fear, and then, starting up, they rushed toward the Superior, huddling together about her, and trying to repress their screams, lest they should be overheard. But it was too late; the footsteps stopped suddenly, strong hands began to tear down the fence close behind us, and the deep breathing of men intent on hard work was plainly audible. It was useless for us to think of escaping them, with the burning Convent in front of us; useless to think of hiding in the garden, which would soon be illuminated in every part by the flames. I looked at the Superior anxiously; brought to bay at last, she opened her mouth to call out, " Who is there ? " I hastily interrupted her, not knowing *what* might happen if *her* voice was heard, and, taking the word from her lips, — with a desperate effort of courage, I confess, — *I* called out, " Who is there ? what do you want ? " A horrible moment of suspense followed, and then a suppressed voice answered, " We are friends ; don't be afraid, we have come to save you." The Superior knew the voice, and exclaimed, joyfully, " It is Mr. Cutler, and his men are with him. O, God be thanked!" she added, fervently. This ejaculation was the only admission of fear or apprehension that she allowed to escape her lips that night in my hearing. " Hush, hush ! " the suppressed voice warned us. " You will be overheard. For the Lord's sake, keep quiet ; them fellows are looking for the Superior already; we were afraid we should be too late." And the tearing and ripping of boards went on furiously. So strongly was the fence built, that it seemed an intolerable length of time before an opening could be made in it sufficiently large for one person to creep through, with aid from the outside, the men having only their hands to work with. There was such a rush of frightened creatures at the opening, each anxious to escape first, and pulling and pushing those who impeded her, that Mr. Cutler had to exert all the authority that could be compressed into energetic whispers before he could bring about some kind of order, and begin to pull us through, one at a time. For my part, I felt myself a heroine; the first distinct cry of the mob on Charlestown bridge, which I heard from my solitary station at the dormitory window, had transformed me into one, though I confess to sundry momentary backslidings into cowardice; and in that capacity I withdrew proudly from the crowd, with my passive little charge, and waited my turn.

There was a great deal of confusion before the terrified company found themselves safe on the right side of the fence, and to facilitate their escape, a man was assisted by his comrades to climb the fence, where he sat astride, pulling up the children, one after another, from the Convent garden, and dropping them down into strong hands, which waited to receive them on the other side. This process took less time than would have been required to make another opening in the fence; but it was an ignominious mode of exit, and showed to great advantage the odd disarray of the children. I could see, for instance, that one had on only a petticoat outside her night-gown, another a nightcap under her bonnet, — for children wore nightcaps in those days. A third displayed one leg bare, with a garterless stocking on the other ; a fourth had a shawl pinned over a flannel skirt ; a stringless shoe and a slipper down at heel clambered over the fence together on one pair of feet.

Suddenly I saw my old acquaintance Mary, putting up her arms imploringly to the man whose leg dangled down above her, as if begging him to help her up next. I had not before observed that she was with us, and I was anxious to know whether she had gone to bed dressed, according to the solemn agreement made between us to that effect on the afternoon previous. Yes, I could see quite plainly, by the light from the burning Convent, that she had kept her word ; up she went in the man's strong grasp, in her pink frock, apparently all right. But she was awkward, and the man who was pulling her by both wrists was in a hurry ; he gave a sudden jerk, the pink frock burst open, and some folds of Mary's nightgown fluttered forth ; her cape-bonnet fell back from her shoulders, and more nightgown was revealed, and as she made an involuntary flying leap over the top of the fence, I saw reason to be con-

vinced that her nightgown was her only garment,
save the treacherous pink frock

"There, Mary's goodness has been too much for
her, after all !" I thought.   She was afraid of offend-
ing Sister Mary Austin.   Well, she 'll never have
another chance, and I suppose she is glad she obeyed
rules up to the last minute, though it has cost her
two petticoats and a pair of pantalets."

Being determined to fulfil *my* promise to keep fast
hold of Louisa's hand till she should be in a place of
safety, I refused to be dragged over the fence in my
turn, but crept quietly through the opening, about the
very last to make my escape, though I must confess
this act of courage cost me a great effort.   And yet,
though in haste to follow my companions, who were
fast disappearing from my sight, as they made their
way down the hill towards Mr. Cutler's house, I turned
and looked back on the Convent through the narrow
gap in the fence, — like a picture of fire set in a
black frame, — and for the first and only time that
night I shed bitter tears.   I did so mourn over the
fate of my poor Claribel, perhaps at that very moment
melting in the flames.   I declare I don't like to think
of the grief I suffered on her account, as I sat, dumb,
on the ground that night in the garden, with my eyes
fixed on what I thought her funeral-pyre ; nor of the
remorse which tortured me in thinking how easily I
could have saved her.

Poor little Louisa looked into my face when she saw me weeping, and I fancied her countenance was troubled; and she made an unsuccessful effort to find her pocket, with the purpose, I do believe, of offering me her handkerchief when she saw me wiping my eyes on the hem of my frock.

We found ourselves in a potato-field, which covered the slope of Mount Benedict, between the Convent and Mr. Cutler's house, which fronted the high-road at the bottom of the hill. Down through the ridges we stumbled, as fast as we could, following the Superior and her little anxious party into the very house where poor Sister Mary John had taken refuge in the delirium of brain-fever. A number of people met us at the door, and without speaking, they led the way at once up stairs, ushering us into a couple of large back chambers, whose windows faced the Convent. There was a high feather-bed in the room which I entered, covered with a patchwork quilt, and I immediately, with a great effort of strength, lifted up my little Louisa, and laid her upon it, that she might rest for a few minutes, at least. I was not used to feather-beds, but I think this must have been a very fine one, for I recollect well how the child sunk down into the midst of the feathers, which rose up all around her and almost hid her from my sight, in the bottom of a little nest, while I stood on tiptoe to peep down upon her like a small mother-bird over a big fledgling.

The older girls generously gave up the bed to the little ones, who clambered up its height, and flung themselves down upon it, in a promiscuous confusion of heads and legs, — like a handful of jackstraws just dropped. The one fixed idea in my mind through the night was, that it behooved me to keep fast hold of my Louisa's hand under all circumstances ; and to effect this, as she lay in the bed, I was obliged to stand on a footstool beside her, and lean my head against the bedpost. Then my eyes naturally fixed themselves on the burning Convent, full in view from the windows, — a magnificent display of fire-works, which illuminated the room, the house, and the neighborhood for a good distance.

I think I must have fallen into a state of semi-somnambulism, a sort of half-awake, half-asleep condition, for I remember gradually losing my identity, and becoming in an odd way *one* with the flames, from which I felt unable to turn my eyes. They appeared to rise and fall with my breath, to pulsate with the beating of my heart, and through the varied noises of the conflagration a voice seemed to be addressing me in an undertone. Yet I was conscious that Sister Mary John had dropped into an arm-chair by my side, and was sitting there absolutely motionless, her long neck drooping forward, and holding the crucifix of her rosary clasped in her hands. Other people moved about the room, talking

in low murmurs; their figures flitted before my eyes,
but I recognized only this one figure of Sister Mary
John, still as a statue. I even lost sight of Louisa's
pale little face, though I knew I was always clasping
her hand. Suddenly I started up, thoroughly roused;
Sister Mary John had flung up her head with a wild
cry, and before I could draw a long breath she had
sprung from her chair, and was running round and
round the room, like an animal in a cage, vehemently
talking to herself in a torrent of meaningless words.
The people in the room shrank away from her for a
moment, but it was evident that she was perfectly
harmless. Delirium had broken out again, and no
wonder. Poor creature! she saw no one, and took
no notice when she was spoken to, but she continued
to run pitifully about the room, still clasping her crucifix. And nobody paid much attention to her; a sort
of apathy had fallen upon us, and we had got used to
horrors. I now think I must have lost myself once
more in sleep after that, for I remember starting up
again, and becoming conscious of a strange apparition. The tall figure of Sister Mary John stood between me and the window, disguised in a large bonnet and a school-girl's cloak that hardly reached her
knees. She was perfectly quiet again, but she trembled all over; she had taken it into her head that the
vengeance of the mob was to fall on her alone, and
that she would be instantly murdered unless she was

8

disguised as a school-girl. She therefore insisted on wrapping herself in a child's cloak, the only garment of the kind possessed by our scantily clothed party, refusing to accept instead one that was offered her by Mrs. Cutler, and which was quite long enough for her.

Mr. Cutler appeared at the chamber door. "Come," said he, hurriedly, in a low voice. "Are you ready? Follow me; for you can't stay here. The mob have tracked the Superior, and they declare she is in this house   I have put them off as long as I can. I dare n't keep you any longer. I and my men will go with you up Winter Hill, and try and find some hiding-place for you. Come, come, no delay." This was the substance of what he said to us; and we were hurried off by the women of the family, who were waiting down stairs to aid our escape. In fact, we were too near the Convent; and there was so much light from the flames that no place of concealment remained for us in its neighborhood.

So I lifted my poor little Louisa out of her nest, and we followed the Superior and the Sisters, who had most of them been hidden in an adjacent room, and who now appeared wrapped in a few shawls and hoods, which did not disguise them much. The poor young Novice tottered down stairs, supported by two of the Nuns, her white veil twisted about her head something in the form of a cap. Just as I was cross-

ing the threshold of the chamber, I stumbled over a
little brown cape, which had been dropped either by
some child who had gone down before me or by some
one in the house. I joyfully picked it up, with no
idea, however, of inquiring for the owner, and fastened
it round little Louisa's neck.

We left the Cutler farm-house as quietly as possible
by the back door, Sister Mary John hurrying on first,
with such odd long strides that two of the older girls,
of whom she had been fond, ran forward to join her
and to take her between them, each holding an arm.
But she was so afraid murderers were pursuing her,
that the girls had hard work to soothe and quiet her.
We blundered along through a back-yard and a field
or two, after leaving the house, and finally emerged
upon the road at some distance from it. The men
who were with us hurried us continually, but, fortunately for the little children, the Superior, who was
stout and wholly unaccustomed to walking, soon got
out of breath, and positively declared her determination to "take it slowly." The men argued in vain.
The Superior vowed she would walk no faster if the
mob were at her heels, and called imperatively on
Sister Mary John to slacken her pace. The poor
lady, accustomed to obey the Superior implicitly, did
so now as long as she could remember the command,
and then hurried forward again. The sick young
Novice, stimulated by fear, and perhaps refreshed by

the open air, felt herself able to walk, but she was
only too happy to creep on slowly between two strong
Nuns; and we poor children dragged our weary
bodies along in straggling procession.   No rioters
appeared anywhere; we were already a good distance
from the Convent, and the Superior, whose reckless
courage never failed her, even at the moment when
she found herself face to face with the mob, began to
laugh and joke with Mr. Cutler and the Sisters about
her, sorely to the distress of our escort, who seemed
to be far more alarmed for her than she was for herself.   At that time there were scarcely any houses
between Mount Benedict and Winter Hill; the few
scattered dwellings being occupied by bricklayers and
laborers, and by no means suitable as places of refuge
for so large a party, even had it been prudent to stop
so near the precincts of the Convent.   Mr. Cutler
made us walk as fast as was possible; he and the
men with him were leading the most backward of the
children by the hand, till we had climbed well up Winter Hill, and were nearly a mile, I should say, from the
Convent.   Here our anxious escort thought it best to
pause and look about for some place where it would
be safe to ask for shelter.   We were passing some
comfortable-looking houses, probably built by people
who wished to command the fine view from the top of
the hill, and Mr. Cutler happened to know some of
their occupants.   So, calling a halt before a substan-

tial dwelling, he went forward himself to the door,
and began to knock and ring, at first softly, and afterwards louder and louder. Then he stepped back into
the front yard, and called up to the chamber window,
addressing the occupants of the house by name. All
in vain ; dead silence prevailed ; the house was shut
up as if it was deserted, every blind closed, and not a
sign of life anywhere. " Well, if that ain't peculiar ! "
I remember Mr. Cutler said to himself, as he slowly
withdrew down the gravel-walk to the gate. " Let 's
try t' other man." " T' other man " lived close by,
and Mr. Cutler made a similar attack on *his* hospitality; but no answer was vouchsafed : the same silence,
the same air of desertion, reigned, not only at Mr.
" T' other man's," but about the neighborhood. It
was like a " deserted village." Mr. Cutler seemed
provoked, as well as astonished, that he could make
no one hear, and this surprised *me.* I thought to
myself, in my simplicity, " Why, if these people have
been able to sleep sound all night, so near the uproar
of the mob and the light of the burning Convent, it
is n't at all likely they could wake up for any noise
Mr. Cutler is able to make ! " I always prided myself on being *reasonable.*

Meantime we grew tired of waiting, and as no one
seemed willing to let us in, we found a temporary
resting-place for ourselves ; we thankfully sat down
on the edge of the sidewalk, and were glad to rest our

heads against the fence behind us. Mr. Cutler urged us to rise, telling us we must " keep moving," till we found some person willing to receive us ; he could only hope that person would be found living within a reasonable distance. And this hope was unexpectedly fulfilled, for just as we were preparing to rise from our comfortable seats, we heard at a little distance the sound of a window opening, and a voice cried, " Who 's down there? What 's wanted ? " We all turned to look in the direction of the voice, and saw a ghostly apparition gleaming white from an upper window of a house at a little distance, whose hospitality Mr. Cutler had not yet sought. It resolved itself into the nightcapped head of an old gentleman, which bobbed up and down, like Punch's, over the window-sill, when Mr. Cutler had made haste to place himself below and begin an eager parley with it. Anxious to hear what was said, I followed our good guide into the small front yard of the house, with my inseparable little companion, and we sat down together under a convenient lilac-bush. Mr. Cutler was trying to persuade the old gentleman to admit us, and shelter us till morning, when the mob, as he said, would certainly disperse to seek its own safety, and the fugitives from the Convent be sought for by their friends and taken away.

The old gentleman said he had been up and about his house all night, — "Strange," thought I, " that he

should be so much more wakeful than his neighbors!"
— very much alarmed by the mob, of whose vicinity
he was aware, and very anxious about the fate of the
women and children at the Convent. He declared
he was thankful for the Superior's escape, but he
was very reluctant to admit her, as he knew her to be
the special object of the hatred of the rioters, though
he made no objection to receiving any number of
children under his roof. But he was a kind-hearted
old gentleman, he of the nightcap, and Mr. Cutler
at last persuaded him to admit us all, assuring him
that we were not followed by any of the mob, who
must have been thrown off the scent, and be looking
after the Superior in another direction, if indeed they
thought it worth while to search for her at all.

So the nightcap disappeared from the window to
reappear at the front door, where it bobbed a hospitable welcome, even to the Superior, who showed herself heartily glad to be once more under a roof. We
all crowded into a little parlor on the right-hand side
of the front door, where an old lady in a ruffled cap
gleamed on the Nuns curiously through a pair of
spectacles. She wished to be kind to them, and she
was very sorry for them, — very sorry, too, to have
them in her house at that time. Yet all honor to
Mr. and Mrs. Joseph Adams of Winter Hill, for they
were indeed good Samaritans, — better than · the
Samaritan, for *his* kindness cost him only time and

money, while *theirs* brought them, as they firmly
believed, into danger, all the more formidable to
their fears because they did not know in what shape
it would come or when to expect it.

And now, while Mr. Adams made haste to bar and
lock the front door, and Mrs. Adams to hide the only
candle she dared keep burning in the house behind
the fireboard of the parlor, the Superior, in her
usual queenly fashion, seated herself right in the cen-
tre of the mahogany horse-hair sofa. It was the most
elegant piece of furniture in the room, and no one
dreamed, though seats were scarce, of sharing it with
her. Sister Mary John was in such a state of restless, nervous excitement that good Mrs. Adams took
her up stairs at once, and tried to quiet her by making her lie down on the bed; on the other side of the
same bed the Nuns laid the poor worn-out young
Novice, — I wish I could remember her name ! — two
sufferers from the effects of this dreadful night's
work, equally exhausted, but showing it so differently.

Meantime I had seated myself on the carpet at the
Superior's feet, with Louisa stretched out on the hearth-
rug, and her head on my knees.

The Superior seemed neither tired nor anxious; she
appeared as fresh as if she had been soundly sleeping
all night in her bed, and perfectly indifferent in regard
to the past, the present, or the future. She was in

reckless spirits, and her lively speeches, which she
tried to utter in whispers, made me laugh. She must
have recognized me as a kindred spirit in courage, for
she did not disdain to amuse me with her banter.
Having occasion to use her handkerchief, she felt in
her deep pocket and brought forth a very dirty one,
and also her snuff-box, which she was delighted to
find there. Her face brightened up. " Old friend, I
did n't forget *you*, then ! " she cried, and eagerly she
took off the cover. Alas, it was empty ! Her countenance fell; I had never seen it wear an expression
of such distress. But recovering herself, and heaving
a comical sigh, she held forth tragically, one in each
hand, her soiled handkerchief and empty snuff-box.
" If I only had a clean pocket-handkerchief and some
snuff," she said, " I should be perfectly happy ! "

Then Mr. Adams entered the room hurriedly, and
implored the Superior to be silent ; he had seen from
the upper window people approaching from the direction of the Convent ; and even as he spoke the sound
of rude talking and snatches of rough singing became
audible. With beating heart I heard the voices and
steps come nearer and nearer, pause, as if for consultation, and finally stop at Mr. Adams's gate. Heavy
feet trampled the gravel-walk which led to the front
door, and the bell rang loud and long, while the feet
shuffled impatiently on the doorsteps. I suppose
there was not a human being in the house who dared

to draw a long breath at that moment. Mr. Adams showed great presence of mind; he let the impatient hands pull the door-bell several times, and paid no attention to the voices which shouted for the " man of the house " to appear. I watched him as he stood in our midst, with his finger on his lip. At last, when the clamor outside could no longer be ignored, he pulled off his coat, drew on his head the nightcap in which we were first introduced to him, appearing all in white down to his waist, like a man just out of bed, and crept softly up stairs. We heard his light foot-steps cross the room overhead, and then the leisurely opening of a window and throwing back of a blind. I suppose the old gentleman never knew before how great a talent he had for acting. With a sleepy air of astonishment and a bewildered manner of speech, just like a man suddenly roused from a deep sleep, he asked what was the matter, and why such a noise was made about his house. A confusion of voices answered him; a great deal of foul language was used that I did not understand, but this was the substance of their errand : They were searching for the Superior; she had been seen going toward Winter Hill; they suspected she might be hiding about the neighborhood somewhere, perhaps in that very house; or, if not, very likely the old man knew something about her. If so, she was wanted, and he 'd better tell all he knew if he had any notion of what was good for

himself.   Mr. Adams eagerly interrupted them by
asking questions, like a man perfectly astonished at
what he heard, and full of unbounded curiosity to
have it explained.   The *Superior* walking up Winter
Hill !   Why, what could they mean ?   And dear me!
there *was* a fire down Charlestown way, and a big
one, too !   When folks shut their blinds before they
went to bed, they could never see anything, nor hear
anything either, especially if folks were getting old
and deaf.   So that was the Convent burning !   Good
gracious! how did it happen?   Well, I want to know!
And good Mr. Adams, acting perfect ignorance to the
life in regard to the night's work, got the fellows below all talking together about it, explaining, answering
questions, boasting among themselves, and contradicting each other, till, being probably half intoxicated
and dull of apprehension, they forgot the purpose of
their visit, and finally went off together, disputing and
wrangling over the events of the night.

All this has taken nearly as long to tell as it did
to happen ; and when, the rioters having gone, Mr.
Adams came down stairs to us once more, after carefully closing his blinds and his windows, and stuffing
his nightcap into a handy pocket, in case it should
be needed again, he could not help modestly admiring his own skill in getting rid of them, even in
the midst of his anxiety on our behalf.   We children
were all conveyed softly up stairs to a back chamber

opposite the one occupied by the Nuns, and as I passed its open door, I saw the poor Novice, white as the pillow under her head, lying with her eyes shut, so deathly still that when, a few weeks afterwards, I heard she was dead, I pictured her to myself, stretched out in her coffin, and looking exactly as I remember her at this moment, when I saw her for the last time. For the last time also I saw poor Sister Mary John, as I glanced through that open door. She was struggling to rise from her pillow, and was gently restrained by the Sisters, who bent over her. She had heard our footsteps as we came up the stairs, and, possessed with the idea that the murderers who had been so long pursuing her had at last found her out, she was full of terror, and I shall never forget the expression of her great haggard eyes as she fixed them on the door, — the last look I ever had of her. The Nuns had ventured to keep a candle burning in the room they occupied, as it fortunately was furnished with window-shutters, which they closed tightly before they dared indulge themselves with a light. By the melancholy glimmer of this one candle these two sad faces, side by side on one pillow, were daguerreotyped on my memory.

I suppose the opposite room, in which we children were crowded together, was good Mrs. Adams's " spare room," for though we were allowed no candle, I perceived through the darkness a glimmering of

pure white all about it, from muslin curtains and
from toilet-covers and "tidies" and towels and a
Marseilles counterpane. Mrs. Adams gently requested us to take off our shoes before stretching
ourselves on this last, and I, finding a vacant spot
near the footboard of the bedstead, made haste to
take it for poor little Louisa's use, and as her small
body occupied but a tiny place, I squeezed myself in,
close to her side, partly for the convenience of holding her hand, and partly because I began to feel inexpressibly weary. The little Southerner was as passive
all night in my hands as Claribel herself would have
been, — she showed no more will or life. The poor
little creature was no heavier than a good-sized doll,
but she was far more badly made; her small skeleton
lacked altogether the plump roundness of finish that
sawdust gives.

"*Will* this night ever come to an end?" I asked
myself, as I lay with my head against the footboard
of the bedstead, trying hard to keep my quivering
eyelids closed, for though I was terribly weary, I had
no desire to sleep. I really had to make an effort to
remember how daylight and sunshine looked. So
many events and so many emotions had been
crowded into the last few hours that I seemed to
have lived a year since the last sunset. "And no
sign of morning yet!" I thought, opening my eyes,
and fixing them on the window to see if there was

any glimmering of dawn. Nothing but the everlasting night was to be seen in the sky, but voices again struck my ear, and the sounds of footsteps drawing nearer and nearer. More rioters, I thought, starting up from the bed. And indeed the bell again rang loudly, and thumps and kicks were bestowed on the front door. And in the midst of the perfect silence preserved in the house I heard Mr. Adams again opening the window and blinds of his chamber, and caught the sound of his voice, addressing those below who had disturbed him. The parleying back and forth between door and window did not last long this time ; of course the visitors were a band of rioters, who had not given up the search for the Superior, and I don't know what number of righteous falsehoods were uttered by Mr. Adams in getting rid of them. They went away, however, and I sank back into my old place by the footboard. The bed was covered with children, and some lay about the floor on the pillows they had taken from it, and I don't remember that they took any notice of this second visit of the mob. I dare say most of them were asleep. And after the intruders were gone I too fell asleep, probably only for a few moments, and my sleep must have been light, for I was aroused by hearing more voices at the front door, more knocking and ringing, followed in due course by the opening of the chamber window, and Mr. Adams's tones of expostulation. But I was very much surprised to hear him suddenly speak in a natural, joyful voice, and then, leaving the window open, hurry down stairs, and actually unbolt and unlock the front door, and fling it wide open! I heard footsteps in the little hall, and afterwards in the parlor below, but I could distinguish no voices, as probably the conversation was carried on in whispers. Who could these strange visitors be, that were so gladly admitted into the Superior's presence?

I was just about to wake Louisa and go down stairs to see for myself what had happened, when Mrs. Adams opened our chamber door and came in gently. " I am awake!" I whispered, jumping off the bed. " Who are those people down stairs, Mrs. Adams?" " I am so sorry to wake up these tired children," she answered, " but I think they ought to know that Mr. B—— and his brother-in-law," — she mentioned his name, but I have forgotten it, — "the fathers of two of the Convent scholars, have just come out of Boston in search of their children, and Mr. Cutler sent them here to look for them." I suddenly remembered that Mr. Cutler and his men had disappeared as soon as they had left us safely housed at Mr. Adams's, — of course to return home immediately and keep guard over their own property. Mrs. Adams went on to say, in the whispered tones we were all enjoined to use, that Mr. B—— and his brother were greatly distressed and disappointed in not finding their children at her house, and on hearing from the Superior that they had never joined her party, and that she knew nothing about them. As they had already made all the inquiries they dared in the neighborhood of the Convent, they now proposed to return to Boston at once, in hopes of finding their daughters safe at home before them. And they offered to take charge of as many of the children whom Mr. Adams was so kindly sheltering as were willing to accompany them. Mrs. Adams roused the girls from their sleep on the bed and on the floor, and made them all understand this offer of Mr. B—— and his brother, patiently explaining it over and over to minds stupefied by so many hours of excitement and fatigue. She was hospitable and thoughtful to the last, assuring the girls that they were welcome to stay at her house just as long as they wished, till their parents and friends should come for them, and bidding them remember that it would not be easy to get to Boston that night, when no carriages could be procured, and the roads might be infested by the rioters. I am afraid we did not pay much attention to Mrs. Adams's prudent remarks ; we all decided to go with Mr. B—— and his brother, — believing, with the faith of little girls, that we should be safe in the company of grown-up men, — all except a few of the children whose homes were at a distance, and who had no friends in Boston.

We did not give much time to preparation for our journey; there was very little to be done. Frocks were tied up and twitched into position; those who had on small shawls brought the two ends round from back to front; and those who still had strings in their shoes laced them up. Those who had bonnets felt themselves to be in full dress, and we bareheaded ones involuntarily shrank behind them, as we stole down the stairs in a little procession, to present ourselves to the gentlemen who were waiting for us.

The Superior, still sitting erect on her sofa, as one whom it was impossible to subdue or fatigue, took very little notice of us, and seemed not to care whether we went or stayed. She was talking volubly to the gentlemen, in low tones of course, but with many emphatic gestures, expressing, as was natural enough, vehement indignation at the treatment to which she had been subjected, and the losses she had been made to suffer. The gentlemen, who would have sympathized with her keenly at any other time, were just then too anxious about their daughters' safety to think of anything else, and they left her abruptly, as soon as the forlorn little group of children appeared in the hall.

Before we quitted the house, careful Mrs. Adams took the precaution of stealing out upon the sidewalk and surveying the road up and down, so as to make sure that the coast was clear for our starting. We

9

left those generous, hospitable people without a word
of adieu, or one expression of gratitude for their great
goodness to us in our misfortunes, and I don't know
whether our parents and friends ever called to thank
them afterwards on our behalf. Nor do I know how
long the Superior and her Community stayed at their
house; but I am sure, from what I heard of her sub-
sequent conduct, that she was a most troublesome and
ungracious inmate, of whom they must have been
glad to be rid.

Mr. B—— crept in behind the parlor fireboard,
just as we were leaving the house, in order to consult
his watch, and great was my astonishment to find it
was only three o'clock when our journey to Boston
began. A journey indeed it proved to be, though Mr.
B—— had intended, when we started, to make it as
easy as possible for our weary little legs by taking us
to Charlestown Street through roads as direct as it
seemed prudent to follow, and then, chartering a stage,
to convey us the rest of the way to the city. Mr.
Adams's house fronted the main road to Boston by
the way of Charlestown, but it led past the foot of
Mount Benedict. As it was the only road to the city
with which Mr. B—— was acquainted, he at first
slowly took his way down the hill, with the intention
of following it, if possible; but when we got near the
bottom of Winter Hill, the light that still blazed from
the burning Convent illuminated a great number of

black figures still surrounding the building, and going up and down Mount Benedict, crowding the turnpike before us, and making a confused, excited murmur of talking and laughing. Perhaps the crowd had been drawn together only by curiosity ; but Mr. B—— dared not venture to pass them with his odd-looking flock of girls, who would be instantly recognized as fugitives from the Convent, and at least exposed to brutal jeers, so he reluctantly turned back, and after ascending Winter Hill again, he plunged to the left into a lane that he fancied would lead us past the foot of Mount Benedict and into the street beyond by a *détour*.

So on we walked and walked in this solitary lane, Mr. B—— and his brother first leading the way, and the children straggling behind in profound si- lence. I still held little Louisa's hand in a tight grasp, and it was lucky for me she was so light and small, as I was obliged to half carry her when her feeble steps failed. Mr. B—— was very patient, and very sure we should come out all right on the main road in time, but evidently we had found the long lane that had no turning, and he grew first anxious and then discouraged, and stopped at last to recon- noitre. We had come to a little bridge which crossed a small stream, and, hanging over this bridge with folded arms, apparently regarding the water, was the solitary figure of a man, as motionless as the fisherman on my mother's Chinese Willow ware plates, who surveys the blue water from the blue bridge in the same attitude. I remember asking little Louisa if she did not see the resemblance, supposing that every family from Canada to New Orleans used Willow pattern plates because *we* did. The poor little thing was getting fretful, and I wanted to amuse her while Mr. B—— was talking with the solitary on the bridge. He was evidently asking the way, and the man, without raising his head, muttered some reply with which Mr. B—— had to be satisfied. When he rejoined us, I heard him tell his brother that the right way to get to Charlestown Main Street from this lane, as well as he could make out from the answers he had received from the man, was by Lechmere Point, and that Lechmere Point was off in *that* direction, vaguely sweeping the dark horizon with his hand.

So we started on our journey again with new courage. I never heard of Lechmere Point before that moment. I have never been there since, and I am sure we did not find it that night, though Mr. B—— continued to walk on and on towards the horizon with the perseverance of the Wandering Jew; and we followed, still in profound silence, our strength kept up in some mysterious way. We all felt that Mr. B—— was doing his very best for us, and that if he had not undertaken to guide *us* he could have gone straight home by the main road, unnoticed by the rioters, if they were still in the neighborhood, so we would not add to his perplexities by our complaints.

We were walking with our faces to the east, and we could see morning coming from a long way off. When the dawn began to glimmer in the sky, it seemed to me like the quivering of a closed eyelid just before it is lifted ; and as the light grew brighter and rose higher and higher above the horizon, this eyelid of night seemed gradually to unclose, till the eye of day looked forth uncurtained. My imagination was stimulated by hours of unwonted excitement, and all manner of strange fancies darted through my brain, as I believe I have made evident enough in the course of this little history.

I think my thoughts as well as my eyes must have been in the sky, for I recollect realizing, with a great start, that we had fairly come out at last on Charlestown Main Street, after losing our way and wandering vaguely about, I knew not where. I am sure the gentlemen who were with us were astonished too, to find themselves unexpectedly exactly where they wanted to be just when they were feeling sure they should never get there ! And it was time the journey should end; some town-clock struck *six* as we crossed the street and hurried into the great paved courtyard of the tavern or stage-house. I was astonished to see the sun shining brightly on houses and shops ; I think

I must have been walking mechanically, with "my heart asleep," as the Irish say, for I had forgotten that *day* was come, and had only been conscious of the relief I felt in the departure of that dreadfully long night. I roused my torpid faculties, and helped little Louisa to climb a flight of steep back stairs, by which somebody belonging to the tavern introduced us all into a large private room. Mr. B—— and his brother, who had been anxious and uncertain and hesitating in manner and speech ever since they left Mr. Adams's house, now brightened up and grew brisk and quick and energetic. They were very thankful that we had got safely to the stage-house before the town had waked up, and while the streets were empty and deserted; they could hardly understand our good luck in finding them so, or why it was that at six o'clock of a summer morning the shops were still shut up and the blinds of the houses closed. The great stage-house itself was not open to the public, and when Mr. B——, who had often stopped there, led us through the courtyard to the back entrance, he was surprised to see the stables closed and the yard empty, save that two or three hostlers lounged about, keeping well out of sight of passers-by. We were told that behind all these bolts and shutters and blinds the people who lived on Charlestown Street were palpitating with alarm and apprehension, expecting every moment the return of the rioters, of whom nothing had been seen since they roused the town by marching through it between nine and ten o'clock of the night before. If we could only keep in advance of them, and leave the stage-house before they came up, how lucky we should be !

The two gentlemen went down stairs to order the stage at once, which was to take us the rest of the way to Boston. They were gone a long time, we thought, as we sat round the walls of the tavern parlor, on two dozen wooden chairs, terribly impatient to be off, and straining our ears to catch the sound of stage-wheels, or the tramp of the rioters, wondering which we should hear first ! We had plenty of time to examine each other curiously by the light of day ; such a forlorn little set of children as we were, — half of us with nothing on our heads but our tumbled hair, which fell in elf-locks round our dusty faces. Down the cheeks of the smallest girls meandered muddy streaks, the marks of tears wiped away with dirty fingers. I don't believe we mustered a couple of pocket-handkerchiefs in the entire party, or half a dozen shoestrings. Some of us dragged our shoes after us slipshod, and both shoes and stockings, and the bottoms of our frocks, were covered with mud from walking through dewy grass and dusty roads. Some garterless stockings had been encumbering the wearers by getting under their heels, and they were tying them up with ravellings from ragged petticoats,

torn either on the bushes or in being dragged over
the Convent fence.   A very few of the children had
made an attempt to save some of their property.   One
girl had her " lap-bag " with her patchwork and silver
thimble ; another, who was dressed more thoroughly
than any of the party, having on frock, bonnet, and
shawl, carried her nightgown rolled up under the
shawl.   This reminded Mary H—— to take off her
nightcap, which she still wore under her bonnet, and
put it in her pocket.   One little girl carried a small doll,
whose head had rolled from its shoulders in the course
of the night, so that the poor little mother sat weeping
silently in a corner ; while my heart ached sympathetically in thinking of Claribel.   Penelope English
had saved a basketful of stockings, the legs of which
hung limp around the sides of the basket.   They reminded me of the dangling necks of dead ducks which
I had seen hanging out of the market-basket at home.
Some milk was brought up for us to drink.   I made
my little Louisa swallow some, and I carried a tum-
blerful to the afflicted mother in the corner, who only
shook her head sadly and pushed it away.   I had
made a bed of two chairs, and a pillow of my lap, for
Louisa, and I felt a great pity for the poor little thing
as I sat looking down into her pale thin face, with
such dark rings round her eyes that the pale blue orbs
looked almost white.   She did not close them, neither
did she appear to see with them.

How glad we were when Mr. B—— opened the
door and summoned us all to get into the stage ; he
looked heated and vexed, for he had great difficulty in
persuading the stage-agent to let us have the use of
his " team," and the coachman had been unwilling to
be seen on the box, and had also needed much per-
suasion. It was no wonder they hesitated, for the
streets began to be filled with ill-looking men returning from the Convent, and they might be ripe for
more mischief when they recognized the passengers
in the stage.

Shut up in the back parlor of the tavern, we had
heard nothing, and when the children found themselves jostled by " rowdy " men as soon as they
reached the street, and saw a crowd of them pouring
along the sidewalk, they would have turned and run
back to the house, had not Mr. B—— insisted on
hurrying us into the stage. He was most anxious to
be at home, looking after his own daughter, and yet
he would not leave us behind him, so he determined
to take the risk of an immediate return to Boston.
We children filled the stage to overflowing, and Mr.
B—— and his brother encouraged the driver by
placing themselves one on each side of him on the
stage-box.

And so began one of the strangest progresses ever
made ; the Convent was mobbed, robbed, and burnt
by a body of from sixty to a hundred men, most of

them Boston truckmen, who had bound themselves to
undertake that work of destruction ; while some *two
thousand* men, old and young, and of all conditions,
stood quietly by and looked on, aiding and abetting
the rioters, because they did nothing to hinder them.
In fact, after the work was done, rioters and specta-
tors must have fraternized in a general *spree*, for they
returned together to the city from whence they came
only when the broad light of day made it unsafe for
them to be found anywhere else.   Our stage drove
from the door of the tavern just as this streaming
tide of rioters was pouring down both sides of the
deserted Main Street of Charlestown ; and of course
the large coach, the only vehicle in sight, attracted
their attention at once.   They had no difficulty in
identifying the passengers ; on account of the heat of
the weather the curtains of the stage had been rolled
up all round and the windows let down, so that the
interior, full of pink calico, and crowded with chil-
drens' heads, half of them bonnetless, was visible to
all.   We looked as ill conditioned as a body of little
paupers broken loose from the almshouse, and those
of the mob who first caught sight of us broke into
loud cheering and rude laughter.   Fortunately it
happened that the crowd was in a mood of high
good-humor, and its heart may have warmed to our
disreputable appearance, so like its own.   At any rate,
the idea of acting as our escort to the city seemed to

seize upon it as a good joke. So we slowly rode the
gantlet between a double file of amiable ruffians, who
saluted us with jeers, yells, shrill whistling, and cat-
calling, roars of laughter, rough jokes, and questions.
Most of them were in their shirt-sleeves ; some, like
ourselves, had no hats ; others had trimmed their
hats with green wreaths, and stuck flowers in their
breasts ; some had red and yellow handkerchiefs tied
round their heads, with a coxcomb or sunflower
stuck in the knot. Some danced and shuffled along
the sidewalk ; others strode on with heads thrown
back. Three or four together, with arms lovingly
intwined, filled the width of the sidewalk here and
there. Some carried a couple of hens, one under each
arm ; some had shawls put across their shoulders,
scarf-fashion, or tied round their waist. " That is *my*
winter shawl," quietly remarked one of the older girls,
breaking the silence in which we were riding along,
and pointing to a burly tall fellow with a tartan plaid
round his body. Luckily he did not see her. Many
mock-respectful low bows were bestowed upon us, and
much wild waving of arms and hands by way of salute.
We scarcely understood any of the questions put to us
in such rough, vulgar utterance as the crowd made use
of, but we did not feel afraid of them ; they were evidently good-natured and meant us no harm. " Saved
yer diamonds ? " shouted one young man to Penelope,
who was resting her basket on the edge of the stage

window. The lovely, fearless girl shook her head, and displayed one of her stockings with a smile ; the crowd applauded vehemently. "I 've got something of yours, I guess ! " bawled out another, holding up his clenched fist to the carriage, which probably contained some valuable which he had stolen. " We 've spoiled your prison for you," cried a third. " You won't never have to go back no more." Indeed, the general sentiment of the mob seemed to be that they had done us a great favor in destroying the Convent, for which we ought to be grateful to them.

How soon we get accustomed to anything, however strange ! By the time our slow driver, who did not wish to excite the attention of the crowd by rapid driving over the stones, had brought us across the bridge into the city, we had ceased to fear this moving procession of rioters or to pay much attention to them. O, how tired we all were ! We thought of nothing but rest, and the girls began to comfort themselves with the reflection that it could not be far off. As for me, I had decided in my own mind to walk out to my home in Dorchester, about two miles and a half from Boston, just as soon as I should have fulfilled my promise to leave Louisa in a safe place ; so I knew that *my* hour of rest was still far off, and I mustered all my resolution to meet the call yet to be made on my strength.

Mr. B——— and his brother, during this strange

drive, had continued to sit one on each side of the coachman, apparently lost in abstraction, or asleep; for they looked neither to the right nor the left, never speaking to each other, or turning to address the children or even the coachman, trying to escape the notice of the crowd by effacing themselves as much as possible. But when our stage had turned off into the city streets, and we had left the body of returning rioters behind us, they quickly recovered speech and energy, urged the driver to speed, and after a deafening, jolting rattle over Boston pavements, the stage drew up at the door of Mr. B——'s house on Pearl Place. Before the gentlemen could jump down from the box seat, Mrs. B—— came running to the door, in hopes of meeting her daughter, who was not with us, and Mr. B——'s disappointment was equal to hers, when he found that she had not yet got home, where he, on his part, had been so long hoping to find her.

We children were kindly ushered up stairs to a parlor well furnished with sofas and chairs, and Mrs. B—— took some of the girls to her own chamber, bidding them lie down and rest for a while. Breakfast, she said, would soon be ready, it was only eight o'clock, and she would let them know when the table was spread. She and Mr. B—— then went away, absorbed in their own affairs. Mr. B——'s brother had already hurried home in hopes of being more fortunate, and finding his own little daughter safe with her mother. I never knew whether it was so, or what befell Mr. B——'s little girl, or what was the fate of the children with whom I had been associated all night. They all vanished out of my life, at once and forever. I had drawn back when Mrs. B——, looking compassionately at Louisa, kindly held out her hand to lead me and my little charge to her bed-chamber, and had said something about making Louisa comfortable enough on the sofa. The little passive thing lay down there as I bid her, and I was delighted to see her actually shut her faded eyes, as if she really meant to go to sleep in the pleasant room whose comfortable appearance seemed to reassure her. I was sure that Mr. and Mrs. B—— would take good care of her, and that, as I seemed to have made no impression on her feeble mind, she probably would not miss me when she waked. Feeling that I had fulfilled my promise to the Superior in regard to her, I withdrew my hand from hers, lingered to kiss her pale forehead and make sure that she was really sleeping, and then slipped out of the room, down the stairs, and out of the house, finding, fortunately for me, the front door ajar.

In a moment I had turned the corner of Pearl Place, into Pearl Street. I knew my way home perfectly; up Pearl Street into High, down High to Summer Street, along Summer to Sea Street, and through the length of Sea Street, out upon the Dorchester

turnpike. Pearl Street was a handsome street, lined
on each side with gentlemen's houses, some of which
had beautiful gardens attached to them. There was
quite a hill to be climbed at the upper end of it,
where it turned into High Street, and up this hill I
toiled as rapidly as possible, for the few people who
met me looked at me with such wonder and curiosity that I was in a hurry to leave this genteel part of
the town and lose myself in the purlieus of Sea
Street. As I have represented myself in the light of
a heroine, through this little history, I am ashamed to
say that in spite of my going to bed dressed, on the
previous evening, I had shown as little forethought in
completing my toilet as the timidest child in school
whom terror had deprived of presence of mind. *I*
was one of the bonnetless company, having nothing
on my head or on my neck and arms. No wonder
people stared! I was unfortunate enough to own a
great crop of coarse hair, a pair of keen black eyes,
and a thin face, still " peaked " from the effects of a
long typhoid-fever. " Dear me," I thought uneasily,
as a milkman, jumping from his cart almost upon my
feet, saluted me with a stare and a prolonged whistle,
" I must look exactly like a weasel peeping from a
brush-heap ! " for I was quite aware of my personal
defects, and that I must be uglier than ever just then
The Boston Athenæum, a handsome stone building,
stood just at the head of Pearl Street, and as I

approached it, I saw, to my consternation, Dr.
A———, our family physician, reading the "Advertiser," at the open window of the Reading-Room ;
he was an elegant gentleman, precise in dress and
manner, of whom I was always a little afraid.   How
devoutly I hoped he would not see me as I passed !
I had lost one shoestring, so that I could not walk
very fast, but I held my head down, and shuffled
along as rapidly as possible, hoping that Dr. A———
would be too much absorbed in his newspaper
to look up.   But I believe that in those days the
"Advertiser" never contained articles of absorbing
interest ; at least the good doctor was not reading
such a one at that moment, for he raised his eyes
precisely as I was passing the window, and fixed
them on me.   He was really too surprised even to
speak for a minute, and I hurried on, pretending not
to see him.   At last, " Louisa Goddard," he cried, in
his loud cheery voice, " what *are* you doing here
at this time of the morning, and where *did* you come
from ? "   I turned short round upon him, and with
a brevity that makes me smile when I think upon it,
I replied, " The Convent was burnt to the ground
last night by a mob, and I am on my way home."
And I whisked round the corner as quickly as possible, running along High Street till my stringless shoe
came off, I was so afraid the doctor would stop me,
and I was bent on getting home at once.

News did not travel very fast at that time, and the destruction of the Convent was not generally known till late in the day. Dr. A—— afterwards said that he was too astounded by my appearance and words to come to his senses till I had disappeared, and though he ran after me bareheaded, — a fact on which he dwelt, as a proof of his determination to overtake me, — I was gone past recall. I felt more at my ease when I got into Sea Street, which swarmed with Irish, as I passed unnoticed among the little Pats and Bridgets that played in the gutter, and crowded the sidewalk in front of the shanties where they lived. I began to feel a great pain in my right hand, — the hand in which I had grasped little Louisa's slender fingers for so many hours ; I had actually strained it badly by this close continued pressure. I rubbed it and shook it, as I walked bareheaded for two good miles, under the morning sun, along Dorchester turn-pike. This turnpike crossed a marsh, and was the highway between South Boston and the country. Tramps, beggars, and evil-disposed persons were always wandering up and down upon it, and though several gentlemen's chaises and carryalls passed me on the road, I was not taken much notice of, I sup-pose because I resembled the foot-passengers they were in the habit of meeting there. Excitement kept me up during that long walk, but as I entered the back gate of my father's yard I felt that I was going

10

to break down. Could it be possible that I was actually at home at that very hour on yesterday morning? I had to search back in my memory to recall the time, for years seemed to have passed since then. I hurried through the kitchen quickly; the cook was washing dishes at the sink, and she too turned and looked at me, as if she saw a spectre. I stopped at the foot of the back stairs and looked up; my mother was just crossing the landing, turning on her hand a clean sock for my father to put on, for she was one of the old-fashioned wives who laid out their husband's clean clothes at the proper times of changing as regularly as they did their baby's.

How well I remember her look and her scream when she saw me, — a scream that was repeated when I slowly ascended the stairs and appeared before her in all my forlornness. "What *is* the matter? How *did* you get here?" she cried, seizing hold of me. I answered her just as briefly as I had answered Dr. A——. "The Convent was burned last night by a mob, and so I thought I had better come home." And then I broke into a violent fit of tears and hysterics. Strange to say, notwithstanding they had been forewarned of the possibility of this event happening, my parents did not believe my statement. My mother was immediately possessed with the idea that I had a brain-fever, — probably the result of my late long sickness, — and that I had

run away from the Convent in that condition. Perhaps a confused recollection of Sister Mary John's
illness haunted her mind. She forbade my speaking
a single word more, though I made desperate efforts
between my sobs, and as soon as I was somewhat
calmed, to get her to listen to my adventures. She
took me into a darkened chamber, undressed and put
me to bed, shut the door behind her, and sent for the
doctor. I fell asleep, of course, fortunately, or I
might indeed have had a brain-fever, and before I
waked the door began to be besieged by officious
friends, who came to let my parents know what had
happened on Mount Benedict. Three of the pupils
died afterwards from the effects of that night's terrors
and exposures, but I remained well enough to enjoy
being the heroine of the family for a time. Indeed,
I had the pleasure of knowing that I was called a
heroine by some others outside the family. Long
years afterwards I heard the story of the burning of
the Convent by a mob repeated by strangers in Cali-
fornia, and the courageous behavior of a little girl
named Louisa Goddard commented upon in terms of
admiration. No one knew that homesickness in my
case was stronger than fear, and that I was glad to
welcome any way of escape from the novelty of Convent restraints. I was too young to understand the
real dangers of the night, and too old or perhaps too
sensible to believe in the imaginary ones. The Supe-

rior and her Community soon after left Boston, dispersing in different directions, and all sorts of scandalous stories relating to their departure were put in circulation. It was fortunate for me they did leave, for my father was determined to send me back as a pupil to an Ursuline school, had the Superior and the Sisters remained to take charge of another, anywhere in the vicinity of Boston.